Off The Grid

Duncan Kerridge

Centre for
Alternative
Technology
Publications

© Centre for Alternative Technology,
1st edition 1995, by Paul Allen and Bob Todd;
2nd edition 1998;
3rd edition 2008, by Duncan Kerridge with David Linsley Hood

Centre for Alternative Technology,
Machynlleth, Powys,
SY20 9AZ, UK
Tel. 01654 705980 • Fax. 01654 702782
www.cat.org.uk

ISBN: 978-1-902175-56-0
1 2 3 4 5 6 7 8 9 10

Printed on 'Regency' Kiara FSC board
and 'Regency' Satin FSC paper in Great Britain by
Cambrian Printers, Aberystwyth. 01970 627111

Published by CAT Publications, CAT Charity Ltd., Registered Charity No. 265239

Mixed Sources
Product group from well-managed
forests and other controlled sources
www.fsc.org Cert no. TT-COC-2200
© 1996 Forest Stewardship Council

Acknowledgements

Thanks to:

Bill Wright, Nick Mercer and Danny Rinky Dink for mobile
inspiration
Dave Roberts, Colin Reading and Richard Stubbs for sound
and light insight
Dan and Frank Jackson for grid connect options
CAT, Dulas Ltd and Techno Tribe for inspiration and facilities
Glynn Morris, Lori, Bridget and Dave for Capetonian thoughts
and facilities
Ketty Dean for research expeditions
Seymour Palmer for processing power
Hugh Piggott and Bob Todd for peer review
Caroline and Graham for pulling it together
And Mary Harris for motivation and infinite patience

Contents

Chapter 1
Why Use Renewable Electricity?

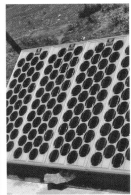

Every day the media assails us with disturbing tales of the environmental and social costs of our obsession with fossil fuels and ever-increasing energy use. Climate change, ozone depletion, hurricanes and floods, corporate sponsored repression of locals unlucky enough to inhabit oil-bearing regions – in the face of this relentless barrage of environmental woe, we often feel powerless to make a difference. But we can play a part in effecting change, by reclaiming responsibility for our energy use. In our high tech, click-and-go consumer culture, one of the most revolutionary acts we can perform is to generate our own energy and grow our own food. This book outlines the information and procedures required to become your own 'energy service provider' using renewable energy.

In the privileged industrialised world, the use of renewable energy is often an ethical, 'lifestyle' choice. However, over 70% of the world's population have no choice but to live 'off the grid', relying on candles, paraffin lamps and batteries for lighting and entertainment. For them, even a single solar PV panel can provide a considerable improvement in living conditions. Slightly larger systems installed at, for instance, a rural clinic can provide lighting for night time treatment and births, and cold chain vaccine storage. In developing countries standalone renewable energy systems are a vital tool for improving conditions and livelihoods in rural areas.

How to use this book

The rest of this chapter looks at renewable energy, its uses and how to purchase and live with a renewable energy system.

Chapter 2 provides advice on how to design your system, and an overview of the different components required.

Chapter 3 discusses loads and how to work out your power requirements.

Chapter 4 shows you how to assess your potential power sources.

Chapter 5 explains how to store your energy using batteries.

Chapter 6 describes how inverters can be used to convert D.C. battery power to mains-like A.C.

Chapter 7 looks at how to control and monitor your system to achieve optimum performance.

Chapter 8 covers wiring design, installation and safety issues.

Chapter 9 considers the special case of mobile power systems.

In general, the earlier sections of each chapter give an overview of the topic suitable for initial enquiries, whilst the later sections discuss more technical details that will help you design the finer points of a system to meet your needs. If the techie bits leave you baffled, don't worry, move on to the next section.

There are also several case studies of complete systems. The first two describe domestic systems using water power and a combination of wind and photovoltaics. The third case study describes a diesel-solar hybrid system installed at a remote Zimbabwean school and the fourth looks at a small system for a mobile home. The examples work through the entire process of design, installation and monitoring so you can see how it is done in practice.

These are followed by a Glossary to explain difficult terms, and Resources pointing you to sources of further information, equipment suppliers and consultants. There are companies that will design, cost and install a system for you, but if you pick up the basic skills and are confident about working with electricity it is possible to do it yourself (making sure, of course, that any system you design conforms to current Building Regulations Part P with regard to electrical installations).

It is beyond the scope of this book to make a detailed examination of photovoltaics, wind turbines and micro-hydro generators. The information provided is intended to help you decide which are the most likely power sources for your application, and how they can fit together. We recommend that you also consult those titles from CAT Publications that cover each form of power in detail.

The energy source of the future

There is no doubt that renewable energy – particularly that derived from the sunshine, wind and flowing water – is the energy source of the near future. Widespread recognition of the full environmental life-cycle costs of nuclear and fossil fuels, coupled with the depletion of natural resources, is making renewable energy an increasingly attractive option.

Many of us can take advantage of this energy on one scale or another. Possibilities include using the sun to heat interiors by optimising building design, installing water heating systems, and, for those with suitable sites, using wind, sun or falling water to provide energy. This book concentrates on using renewable energy to generate electrical power for small-scale applications.

Using a renewable energy source can save money and provide considerable satisfaction. For those who enjoy tinkering with technology there is great scope for fun. In some cases there is also a possibility of selling surplus power through the grid to an electricity supply company. Renewable energy can be an invaluable tool for developing remote power systems where grid supplies do not exist.

To develop a renewable energy system, the site must be assessed for suitability, the generators chosen, the system designed, components chosen and bought, installed and maintained. Systems may be designed for buildings, boats, caravans, motor homes and other small-scale applications. This book covers all of these topics and complements companion titles from CAT Publications, which cover in more detail the assessment and exploitation of energy sources such as wind, water and solar, generators and site assessments; these also include pertinent case studies. These publications are referred to in the text for further reading, are listed in the Resources section, and can be ordered from CAT Mail Order (www.cat.org.uk/catpubs tel. 01654 705959). The Centre for Alternative Technology runs regular courses on renewable energy systems; please call for details or see the website (www.cat.org.uk/courses tel. 01654 705981).

The topic may appear daunting to begin with but the most vital aspect is to keep in mind what you want from your system and the nature of the limitations or possibilities. If you feel you are becoming bogged down by what is at times highly technical material – don't worry; there are many places where you can seek help – not least from CAT! Thousands of people throughout the world rely on standalone renewable energy systems. This book attempts to present some of the lessons learnt by practitioners in the field to help you follow in their footsteps.

Advantages of renewable energy systems	
compared to diesel	disadvantages
no fuel bills	intermittent supply in some cases
less pollution	higher installation costs
less noise	
less likely to break down	
reduced routine maintenance	
longer life	

What is renewable energy?

A renewable generating system produces energy from sources that are constantly and naturally 'renewed'. Such sources include wind, water and solar energy. Whatever type of renewable energy (RE) you use, the original source of the energy is always the sun.

The sun produces energy by a process called 'nuclear fusion', one of the most mysterious and fascinating processes known to humankind. Matter itself is converted directly into energy according to Einstein's famous law $E=mc^2$, where E is the amount of energy created, m is the mass of matter destroyed and c is 3 x 108 metres per second – the speed of light. It can be seen from this equation that a small amount of matter can yield an enormous amount of energy! In fact, the sun generates an incredible 3.94 x 10^{23}kW of power all day, every day.

This radiated energy takes about 8 minutes to cover the 93 million mile journey to reach us on Earth. The total energy reaching the surface of the Earth is about 80,000 x 10^{12} watts, of which about one fifth falls on land. This is still around 1600 times the total world energy demand, equivalent to 170 million barrels of oil per day! Some of this energy can be directly converted to electricity by photovoltaic generation systems. Most is spent on heating up the surface of the Earth, giving rise to the global wind patterns which are exploitable by wind turbines, windmills and wave machines. The remaining four fifths of solar energy falls directly on water surfaces and, with the wind, causes evaporation, leading to rainfall. By collecting energy from rivers and streams we can generate electricity from hydro-power.

Renewable energy sources compared			
	Wind	**Solar**	**Hydro**
Cost of installation	medium	lower	higher*
Site specificity	medium	low	higher
Seasonal variablility	medium	very high	medium
Running cost	medium	low	low
Noise	yes	no	very little
Reliability	medium	high	high
Capital cost	medium	high	lower
			*unless renovating existing systems

Why use renewable energy?

Huge areas of the world require the economic developments enabled by reliable and cost-effective electrical power. To satisfy this demand with nuclear and fossil fuels would place a terrible burden upon the planet, not least because of the effect on global warming. Global concern is increasing over climate change caused by emissions of greenhouse gases such as carbon dioxide from coal and oil fired power stations.

In many parts of the world the population is widely dispersed, making grid-supplied electricity expensive and impractical. Often, the only economic means of generation is on a building or village level basis. A common alternative to grid connection is the use of diesel generators. This is frequently inappropriate, as average electrical loads tend to be much smaller than the rated capacity of the generator, giving very poor overall system efficiencies. Although the initial capital outlay for diesel generators is generally lower than that required for renewable-based systems, the substantial recurrent costs of fuel, operation and maintenance can double the overall cost. In remote areas, particularly in developing countries, regular fuel supplies can be problematic. Consequently, renewable energy can provide a cost-effective alternative for decentralised electricity generation when project costs are examined over the full design life of the generating system. After all, the cost of the energy itself is zero.

In the UK, economies of scale make electricity bought from the national grid the cheapest. However, the costs of a new connection to the grid system are now quite high, often in the region of £6,000 to £25,000. This is leading an increasing number of people who are considering grid connection to seriously examine the alternatives.

Can renewables be used in Britain?

Britain has a long history of successfully using renewable energy. The wind has powered sailing ships for centuries. On land also, windmills and water mills have provided power for water pumping, corn grinding, cotton spinning and, more recently, electricity generation.

Britain and Ireland have the richest wind and rainfall resources in Europe. Hydroelectric power already makes a significant contribution to electricity generation in Scotland. The technologies to capture these resources are available and proven; it is the economics of generation that creates barriers to their wider implementation. Because the economies of scale make grid electricity cheap and reliable it makes sense to use it when it is available. However, in off-grid applications hydro-power or wind hybrid systems can provide a cost-effective alternative in many parts of Britain.

On or off the grid?

In the UK, many people interested in renewable energy are already connected to the national grid. In almost all such cases, it is far cheaper to buy grid electricity than to generate it yourself. However, there are a number of ways to reduce your dependence on the grid.

Efficiency

It is possible to make significant reductions in your energy demand by, among other things,

- installing or increasing roof insulation
- insulating hot water tanks and pipes
- reducing thermostat and timer settings for central heating – reducing the thermostat by 1ºC can reduce a fuel bill by 10%
- fitting double glazing and draught-proofing
- replacing incandescent bulbs with compact fluorescent lights which use 80% less energy
- using a hot-box (or hay box) when cooking
- using 'economy' (or cooler) settings on washing machines
- only boiling as much water as you need in the kettle
- using a modern, efficient fridge-freezer.

There many other measures that may be taken; these are described in depth in *The Energy Saving House* (see Resources).

Solar water heating

A large proportion of domestic energy demand is for water heating. Solar water heating systems are now well established in Britain and have been shown to pay for themselves in six to twelve years. Home-made versions are far cheaper at the cost of increased maintenance and reduced efficiency. *Tapping the Sun* and *Solar Water Heating: A DIY Guide* explore the possibilities for domestic applications (see Resources).

'Green' electricity on the grid

Since the privatisation of the British electricity supply system, large-scale power users (>100kW) have been able to choose from whom they purchase electricity. Legislation has now also de-restricted the domestic power market enabling consumers to pick and choose their electricity supplier. Many offer various 'green' electricity options, which generally fall into two categories.

Green sources

Electricity retailers supply power generated by renewable energy sources. In fact, it is impossible to identify the precise source of the electrons supplied, but the retailer undertakes to purchase an equal amount of power from renewable suppliers as the consumer uses. In most cases, the unit price is slightly higher than that for conventional sources. The exact definition of 'renewable' varies – some suppliers only use wind and hydro, others include solar, biomass, landfill biogas and, somewhat controversially, waste incineration.

If opting for a green electricity tariff, enquire as to what sources are used, and the percentage of the electricity that will come from renewables. There are several companies that offer 100% green electricity tariffs, and although the cost might be slightly more per unit, you will reduce the related emissions from your electricity consumption for the cost of an extra couple of pounds each month.

Green funds

The alternative approach is for consumers to pay a supplementary charge (either per unit or monthly) that goes into a fund for the development of new renewable generation capacity. The fund is usually administered by an independent trust, and may invest in new installations and research into new technologies. Most retailers undertake to match the funding from consumers. As well as electricity supply companies, other organisations such as the Wind Fund enable consumers to invest in the development of renewable energy sources.

Similar green power schemes have been running for some time in USA, where a key issue contributing to consumer confidence is certification guaranteeing that retailers are living up to their promises. The accreditation role in the UK is performed by OFGEM.

There are many issues to consider when choosing a green power scheme. Although source schemes are more immediately green, the

Windfarms feed renewably generated electricity into the National Grid.

fund schemes may be more effective at encouraging the growth of renewable grid electricity. Check all the available options, bearing in mind that prices may vary depending where you live. Important criteria that may affect your choice are:

- actual mix of renewable energy;
- retailer's future targets for renewable energy production;
- retailer's general environmental / social policy;
- environmental / social policy of parent company;
- energy efficiency products or services included in tariff; price per unit.

More information about green power on the grid is available from the office for electricity regulation (OFGEM), the Energy Savings Trust and other groups such as the Consumers' Association and Friends of the Earth.

Selling power to the grid

In the US, Japan, Denmark and Germany, among others, there are growing numbers of domestic renewable power producers with photovoltaic roofs, or small wind or hydro turbines. They export surplus power to the public utilities, either to reduce their own grid electricity bills, or even to make a profit. In the UK, the deregulation of the electricity industry has supposedly made it possible for any

9

power producer to sell electricity through the grid. However, in practice this has only been a viable option for those with access to a considerable energy resource, such as a large falling stream or a windswept hilltop, and the capital to exploit it. There are signs that the situation is changing to enable small power producers to sell direct to power supply companies.

There are several approaches for linking your own system to the grid, all of which will involve negotiation with the regional electricity company (REC), and possibly with a third party power purchaser.

The first option involves feeding power from your system 'upstream' of the company meter. This still requires an approved grid-link inverter and various safety measures, but can simplify the negotiations as you are only substituting your own power in place of that from the grid, but not actually selling any power.

A second option, available in some countries for many years, is just starting to appear in the UK. This entails negotiating a power purchase agreement with the REC or third party power company whereby they agree to buy your exported power at a specified price. If you are selling to the same company that supplies you, this could be a 'net metering' arrangement where what you export commands the same price as what you import. You pay, or are paid, for the net difference.

Alternatively, you may just sell your exports with no link to what you import from the grid. These arrangements are the most common for small-scale generators. Unfortunately, they work out best for the company buying the electricity as you get paid one rate for the electricity you sell and pay another (higher) price for the power you buy.

With the increase in demand for green grid power, there should be a growing market for small independent power producers.

Applications of renewable energy

In this book we are concentrating on the off-grid, standalone applications of renewable energy, suitable for domestic systems. However, it is worth remembering that renewable sources are playing an increasing role in generating electricity for the national grid, just as conventional power stations do.

Government policy

Government policy has changed considerably over the past 15 years as the situation has evolved with regards to the environment and energy policy.

Concern over global climate change due to carbon dioxide emissions from fossil fuels and a political desire to make nuclear power appear commercially viable led the UK government to introduce the 'Non-Fossil Fuel Obligation' (NFFO) in the early 1990s. This obliged regional electricity companies to purchase a percentage of their electricity from non-fossil fuel sources, and offers a financial subsidy to encourage this, derived from an 18% tax on electricity bills.

In 1999 and 2000, the Government proposed two new measures to replace the NFFO and encourage further commercial development of renewable electricity production. The first was the Renewables Obligation Order (ROC) requiring all electricity supply companies to source a specified proportion of their power from renewable sources, and putting in place the ROC system for trading renewable electricity generation credits. This set a target of 10% generated from renewables by 2010. The second measure was the climate change levy, an energy tax to be applied to industry, commerce and the public sector. Renewable energy and combined heat and power schemes are exempt, so this will tend to reduce the price of green electricity relative to other sources. Both policy measures were designed to stimulate a market-led growth in the renewables sector as an important component in the national strategy to reduce carbon dioxide emissions. The Government published its Energy review, 'The Energy Challenge' in 2006. This looked more favourably on small-scale renewable energy projects and has sparked a series of further studies and consultations. One of the most relevant and long awaited is the amendment to microgeneration planning rules, which should remove some of the red tape surrounding domestic renewable energy installations. The 2007 budget to zero-carbon homes is also hoped to lead to greater ease and fluidity for renewables projects.

This serves to show the changing nature of policy. What is clear is a gradual progression towards the acceptance of small-scale renewable generation in this country, although it has been some time in the making and will continue to be subject to moving goalposts for the foreseeable future.

Standalone power

Typical off-grid, domestic applications of renewable generated electricity include providing power for homes, caravans, boats and motor homes. In the UK, boat owners are amongst the most common users of an off-grid renewable energy. Special wind turbines and PV modules that withstand marine conditions are available for use on boats.

To be economic, a system should be sized to produce electricity for equipment that cannot be powered by any other means. In a typical system, renewables would provide power for lighting, music systems, extractor fans, computer equipment, a television and video or dvd player, and possibly refrigeration, with occasional use of power-hungry equipment such as electric drills, vacuum cleaners, etc. In general, it is not cost effective to power heating loads such as cookers, kettles, water and space heaters with renewably generated electricity. The power to run one electric hotplate, for instance, is equivalent to that used by about a hundred high efficiency light bulbs. These loads are best met by other

This yacht is using two 60 Watt Ampair marine wind turbines to charge batteries for lighting, entertainment, communications and navigation systems.

A photovoltaic array powers a satellite communications system in Peru.

means such as solar water and space heating, wood stoves and LPG (bottled propane/butane) cookers. An exception to this rule occurs in AC hydroelectric systems and with some larger wind turbines where the system controller needs a dump load to dissipate excess power. Water and space heaters are often used for this purpose. The amount of energy available depends on the resource and the generator used to convert it.

Apart from domestic and leisure applications, there is also a wide range of commercial and industrial uses for electricity generated from RE sources. Such applications include supplying remote power for communications systems and microwave repeaters, cathodic protection units to prevent rusting of pipelines and well heads, telemetry, electric fencing, medical refrigeration, lighting systems and navigational aids such as aircraft obstruction lighting, maritime buoys and fog warning systems.

Safety
We are all aware that electricity can be dangerous. When you start generating your own power, there are many new risks unknown to the grid-connected. Understanding these, and knowing when to seek advice, is your responsibility to yourself and those around you.

- AC voltages carry shock and fire risks – wiring and appliances should meet standard regulations.
- Batteries contain considerable amounts of energy and highly corrosive sulphuric acid.
- Rotating equipment such as wind generators and water turbines are mechanically hazardous.
- Mountings and towers must be secure.

Battery and installation safety are covered in greater detail later. If you're unsure about anything, get expert advice.

Buying a system

Funding and grants

Renewable energy systems are not cheap, particularly when compared with the unit costs of mains electricity, gas and fossil fuels. There is growing popular and institutional concern over the effects of fossil fuel and biomass use and its effect on the environment and global climate. Initiatives at all levels have been established to promote the use of renewable energy sources. Many countries from both industrialised and developing worlds offer tax breaks, duty-free imports, subsidies and soft loans to encourage renewable energy use at all scales. Among many others, the United Nations Development Programme and European Commission provide funding for developing countries to develop renewable sources to help supply their rapidly expanding energy requirements.

Unfortunately, in the UK there have been few government initiatives to promote this technology. For many years, the main effort was focused on large-scale energy production in the form of the Non Fossil Fuel Obligation described above, and schemes such as the Large Scale PV Demonstration Programme. This was followed by Clear Skies as a funding method for both large- and small-scale projects.

At the time of writing, the current grant scheme in the UK for renewable energy schemes is the Low Carbon Buildings Programme (LCBP), which replaced the Clear Skies grant scheme. It is split into two streams; Phase 1 for householders, community groups and small businesses, and; Phase 2 for public sector buildings (including schools, hospitals, housing associations and local authorities) and charitable bodies.

Phase 1 is administered by the Energy Savings Trust (EST) and there are distinct limits for the grant available for each RE technology dependent on the size of the system. It is split into two areas, Stream 1 for householders and Stream 2 for business and community groups. The EST requires the work to be undertaken by accredited installers and from a given list of products, and has set a basic level of energy saving measures which must be undertaken before the applicant is eligible for a grant. These are:

• at least 270mm of roof insulation;
• thermostat and timer on any heating system;
• cavity wall insulation (if possible);
• energy saving light bulbs in all fittings.

These should be regarded as the minimum level of energy saving and applied wherever practicable.

Phase 2 is administered by the Buildings Research Establishment (BRE), and the level of work is funded as a percentage of the entire cost of the renewable energy installation.

In a few specific cases, trusts occasionally grant funds for community orientated projects. Lottery funds might also be available for public applications and rural and business development boards may support initiatives from businesses. A number of academic institutions are involved in research projects involving both commercial and domestic systems.

The Government has also reduced the VAT on professionally installed RE systems to 5%. However, in comparison to other countries with thriving renewable energy industries, these grants and concessions are small and inconsistent. It remains to be seen whether the Government's professed concern over climate change will result in any serious support for small-scale renewable energy generation in Britain.

Sources of new equipment and expertise

There are numerous companies and organisations offering services and equipment in the renewable energy field, many of whom are listed in the CAT Information Department's database – call 01654 705989 for details of organisations in your local area. They can do everything from supplying equipment to your specifications to designing and installing a whole system from scratch. Obviously, the more they do, the more they charge.

Complete systems

Even if you do not feel confident to design your own system, it will be well worth your while to work through this book to get a basic understanding of the principles involved. Before contacting companies for advice and quotes, it is a good idea to:
- prepare a rough load profile (see Ch. 2);
- ascertain the most promising energy resource/s for your site (see Ch. 4);
- consider how much you can afford to spend;
- get an idea about the function of different system components such as generators, batteries, controllers and inverters.

Providing these details will help a company to make some rough estimates of what you will need. However, particularly for hydro and wind systems, they will probably want to visit your site before finalising a design. It is normal to charge for such a visit, but some companies may discount this cost against that of the whole system should you contract them to supply it. Obviously, it makes sense to get rough quotes from several companies to compare not only costs but also the sizing of components.

Possible questions to ask potential system suppliers include:
- what guarantees are offered for components and the system as a whole?
- what maintenance is required?
- what technical back-up is available?
- what is the design life of the key components, especially the batteries?
- what data and criteria were used for assessing resources and loading?

Component suppliers

If you feel happy to design your own system, you will need to contact potential suppliers for information about their products in order to assess how they will perform and what they cost. Discuss your design and assessments as they may be able to offer advice relevant to their products. With the exception of the last point, the questions listed above are equally relevant for component suppliers.

Installation
A practical enthusiast with a basic understanding of electrical wiring should be able to install small PV arrays and wind turbines, but for larger, more complex systems, particularly those with wind turbines rated over 300 watts or micro-hydro generators, it is best to seek professional assistance for installation. If you are using an AC system, a qualified electrician should certify the wiring before commissioning (see Ch. 8).

Second-hand and scrap
If you have the time to seek them out, there are many bargains to be found at scrap and surplus dealers, and in the classifieds. Since such equipment is usually 'sold as seen', generally without documentation, it helps to have a good idea about what you require. As ever when purchasing second-hand equipment, it is a case of 'buyer beware'. Much of what you may need is someone else's junk – you just have to find it!

Batteries
These offer excellent potential for savings. There are numerous sources of second-hand deep-cycle batteries from applications such as back-up and uninterruptible power supplies, and electric vehicles. Since it is difficult to ascertain their internal condition, it is important to know the source and former use of the battery. Chapter 5 gives advice on what to look for. Second-hand batteries will not last as long as a new set, but can reduce the initial start up cost giving you time to save up for better quality replacements.

Cabling and switchgear
Second-hand cable is widely available at scrapyards and during building demolition and refurbishment. Ensure that insulation is undamaged and that the cable has not been strained. Old consumer units with fuses are also good demolition finds and junk shops may be a source of old meters and fuse boxes. Low-voltage applications such as vehicles, aircraft and military equipment are good sources

of switchgear, relays, large diodes and meters.

Photovoltaics (PV)

In the UK, there is very little market in second-hand PV modules. Second-hand stalls at 'green' festivals sometimes have re-framed amorphous panels. Bear in mind that amorphous panels have a limited life. Manufacturers occasionally have seconds, demonstration and test modules but rarely advertise the fact. Ask around.

Wind turbines

The situation is similar to that for PV. However, it is very possible to build your own wind turbine using an old dynamo or permanent magnet motor; *Windpower Workshop* (see Resources) gives details of how to go about this. Old galvanised water pipe and scaffold poles have excellent potential for use as guyed towers.

Hydroelectric

In the USA there was great interest in small wind turbines between the 1930s and '50s before many remote areas were connected to the grid. In the damper climate of Britain, a similar situation existed in many remote, hilly areas with micro-hydro systems commonly in place. Occasionally, turbines can be found in local classified adverts. Beyond this, a degree of detective work is required. Ordnance Survey maps often mark old hydro installations, and some long established manufacturers still have records of former installations. Old generators and motors suitable for conversion, and old pipe, can often be found in large scrapyards. Certain types of pumps can also be run 'backwards' as turbines.

Inverters

Given the widespread use of inverters in back-up power supplies and military systems, scrap dealers, particularly those carrying old electronic equipment are worth contacting. *Exchange & Mart* and similar publications often carry adverts, too. Be aware, however, that many applications use far less efficient devices than those desirable for renewable power systems.

Living with your system

Generating your own electricity from renewable sources is rewarding and satisfying and can be quite fun, too! The pleasure is increased if you have had a hand in designing or installing the system yourself – with the added bonus that you will understand better how it all works. Modern systems are designed to be as automatic and self-reliant as possible, but a basic understanding of how the system operates will prove invaluable should any problems occur. Such problems can range from a simple blown fuse to leaves in your hydro intake.

Remember, no system can be totally and eternally reliable; the more you understand about your system the easier it will be to live with. Understanding your system will also help you spot potential problems, such as wear in bearings or failing battery cells, before they become too serious. If your system is professionally installed it is essential that you get a full briefing on what it should do and when routine checks and maintenance should be made. A well designed and properly installed RE system can add extra value and appeal to your property, particularly with the increasing number of environmentally aware buyers.

As time goes by you will gain a working knowledge of how best to live with your system, gaining a feel for how much energy is available, how much you have stored and how quickly different appliances use it up. Even a well designed system will occasionally shut down. You must be prepared for the odd hydro intake blockage or windless week – but then even the mains go down from time to time. Be prepared for the unexpected blackout by keeping a rechargeable torch in a place where all the household can find it, and a stock of candles to ensure you'll never be left totally in the dark.

Chapter 2
Basic System Design

The design of an off-grid power system is essentially a problem of matching supply to demand.

How can you extract enough energy from your surroundings to fulfil your requirements?

How can the energy be stored between times of surplus and periods of peak loading?

How can you satisfy your needs and wants with limited financial resources?

The following chapter outlines the design process required to answer these questions. The chapters that follow then go on to examine each of the key elements of the power system in greater detail.

Even if you decide to entrust the design and installation of your system to a specialist company, an understanding of the way in which it all fits together will give you a much better idea of what you can, and cannot, expect from a viable off-grid power system.

The design process

When planning a small-scale renewable energy (RE) system, there is often a tendency to concentrate on the energy generator. This is only part of the story; the rest of the system also needs careful consideration, which is particularly important when costing your project. The main areas to examine are:

- reducing and assessing your loads (Chapter 3);
- discovering the extent of your energy resource and whether it can meet the demands of the load (Chapter 4);
- storing the energy until it is needed (Chapter 5);
- deciding if your system is to be AC or DC and converting between the two (below and Chapter 6);
- carrying the power from the generator to the loads (Chapter 8);

Is renewable electricity easy to understand?

The simple answer is yes! Anyone with a basic understanding of electricity can understand how it is generated in RE systems. Here are some of the most important terms you will need to know :

Voltage is the electrical potential across any two points in a circuit, such as the terminals of a battery or diesel generator. It is the push that makes the electric current flow around the circuit. It is measured in volts (V).

Current is the amount of electricity flowing through any wire or appliance. It is measured in amps (A).

Alternating current (AC) simply means that the direction of the current reverses at frequent, regular intervals. It most often occurs in mains-type applications – e.g. the UK mains supply is described as 50 hertz (Hz) AC, which means that the direction of the current changes through one forward and backward cycle 50 times every second.

Direct current (DC) means that the direction of the current does not reverse. It most often occurs in applications involving batteries, as they can only store direct current.

Electrical power: (measured in watts[W]) is the rate of delivery, or consumption, of electrical energy at any instant. For example, a more powerful lightbulb will be able to give off more light, but at the cost of consuming more power. The electrical power of a device is the product of voltage across it multiplied by the current through it:

POWER = VOLTAGE x CURRENT

W = V x A

Electrical energy (measured in watt-hours [Wh]) is the total amount of electricity produced or consumed in a given period. It is the product of the power multiplied by the length of time the power is produced or consumed.

ENERGY = POWER x TIME

Wh = W x hours

1000W is known as a kilowatt (kW)
1000Wh = 1 kilowatt-hour (kWh) =
1 unit of grid electricity

• providing control equipment to keep the system working correctly, efficiently, safely and automatically (Chapter 7).

Developing a suitable system combining reliability, convenience and economy generally involves a process of iteration, estimating resources required to meet expected loads, then reassessing the load requirements until a cost-effective compromise is reached. The flowchart shown on page 24 outlines the main steps involved.

Will you need batteries?

Batteries form the heart of many systems, yet they are expensive and will need replacing every few years. They are needed to 'level out' the electricity supply, by storing electricity when supply exceeds demand and until demand exceeds supply. They also provide a steady output voltage which allows equipment to work reliably. Although they are useful, if you can avoid using them then all the better. There are two main ways of doing this.

Using a grid-linked system.

If you already have a connection to the national grid and have a contract to supply electricity, you can use the grid in place of a battery, selling electricity to it when you have a surplus and buying it back when you have a deficit. A number of devices exist to make this easier, cheaper and more reliable. Several inverter manufacturers supply units designed for grid connection, but you should consult your REC to check that these are approved for use with their system. At present, any inverter that connects to the grid must meet Engineering Requirement G83 (or G59 for systems larger than 16A pre phase). Contact the CAT Information Department (tel. 01654 705989) for details of suppliers.

Using a hydro-power system.

Hydro-power systems have the distinct advantage of being able to store and regulate the energy before it is converted to electricity. Even without a storage reservoir the power output will not fluctuate as rapidly as wind or solar power systems do. If it is possible to build even a small reservoir, you can store surplus energy before it is converted, further improving the supply reliability.

Examine the Brook family's system described in Case Study 1. A single phase AC generator is driven directly from a high speed turbine such as a Pelton wheel. Electronic control equipment such

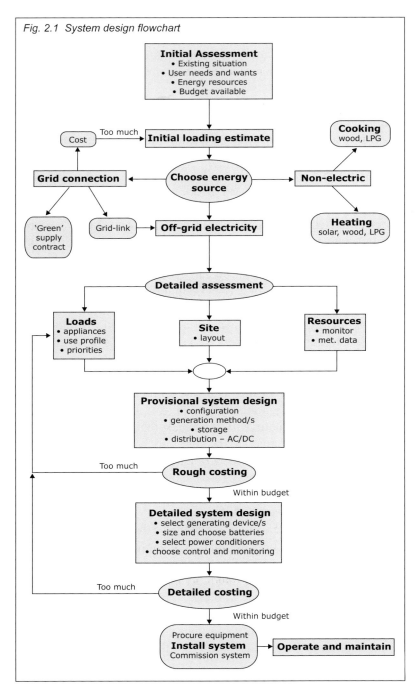

Fig. 2.1 System design flowchart

as the automatic voltage regulator and the load controller ensure the output power is of the correct voltage and frequency. A small reservoir above the water inlet can act as an energy store, removing the need to use batteries.

AC or DC

Most hydro systems do not use batteries and are usually (excepting very small hydros) 240V AC because the resource is continuously available to supply power. For other systems you will almost inevitably have to use batteries and low voltage DC (12 or 24 volts) at some point, as this is the only type of electricity that batteries can store. The only exception to this is if your system is to be connected to the mains electricity supply, so that when your supply runs down, you can supplement it with mains power, and when you have too much you can sell it to the local electricity company.

Many small RE systems operate purely on low voltage DC for simplicity and economy. However, this precludes the use of standard AC appliances, requiring DC versions instead which, though generally more efficient, are often more expensive and hard to find. In larger systems the use of a low voltage supply requires thick cables to keep losses down. For a given power requirement, if the voltage is low, the current must be high to compensate (Power = Voltage times Current), and the power losses in the cable are proportional to the square of the current (see Chapter 8 – Installation and Wiring).

If an AC supply is required, a device called an inverter will be needed to convert the battery DC output to higher voltage AC. This allows the use of standard appliances and wiring at the expense of extra cost and inefficiencies. Inverters have to be sized to meet peak loads, which means that much of the time they may be operating inefficiently at a fraction of their maximum output. In addition, the output waveforms of many inverters can cause problems for sensitive appliances. These issues are covered in detail in Chapter 6 – Inverters.

Choosing the system voltage

When designing the battery store, you will need to choose its operating voltage. The standard value is 12V. However, as mentioned above, larger systems require very heavy, and expensive, cables to keep losses down. In general, it is advisable to keep currents in any circuit below 20 amps. If the voltage is 24V this allows twice the power to be transmitted as at 12V for the same loss. However, it is harder to find appliances to run on 24V, and more expensive to upgrade the system, as pairs of PV modules have to be added to achieve the operating voltage required. Conversely, many larger wind turbines operate at 24V.

For AC systems, it is worth noting that larger inverters tend to operate at 24, 36 or even 48V (for ~ 4kW) to keep input currents down.

General guidelines

- Consider the operating voltage of your generating sources – two 12V (nominal) PV modules can be wired in series to supply a 24V system, but a 24V wind turbine cannot be used on a 12V system.
- It is more convenient to run small DC systems (up to, say, 500W peak supply) at 12 volts.
- If higher power is required, or long cable runs that would be unacceptably expensive for 12V are involved, opt for 24 volts.
- If AC equipment is essential, or where very long transmission lines (100m +) are needed consider an AC based system, perhaps combining two inverters to optimise efficiency by using one for low loading and adding the second to meet peak demand.
- An alternative to AC transmission for a dispersed layout is to use several autonomous low voltage systems.
- Where future (or present) grid connection is anticipated, consider an AC system to standardise wiring.
- If a high power AC supply (2kW +) is needed, the necessary inverters will probably require a battery bank of 24 to 48 volts.
- Where loads are mixed, e.g. overnight lighting, TV and video, a combination of 12V DC and an inverter for AC will be an efficient solution.

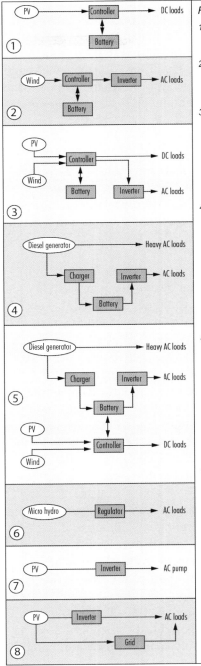

Fig. 2.2 System configurations

1. *A simple DC-only system suitable for domestic lighting, small TV and stereo, and perhaps other DC appliances.*

2. *Where AC appliances form most of the load and power has to be transmitted between dispersed load centres, an inverter-based system is required.*

3. *In many systems a combination of different sources and loads are required. By using different sources, reliability is improved and battery size can be reduced. An inverter supplies essential AC loads, whilst efficiency benefits from the use of DC for low, continuous loads such as lighting.*

4. *Although it does not use renewable energy, the 'genset plus battery' system is a good way to improve efficiency and lifetime whilst reducing fuel costs in situations where a genset is rarely run at full load. The genset operates heavy loads e.g. pumps, whilst also charging the batteries. Prolonged periods of low power for loads such as lights and TV are supplied from the battery via an inverter without running the genset.*

5. *The logical extension to the 'genset plus' system is to add a few PV modules and a wind turbine to reduce the need to run the genset just to charge batteries. The use of some DC loads also improves efficiency by reducing the need to run inverters at low power. This configuration is ideal where there are occasional high power loads such as pumps and welders but most demand is for lights and a few low power AC appliances.*

6. *Micro-hydro systems producing 2kW or more usually supply AC directly to the loads. A voltage regulator keeps the supply constant and safeguards the loads.*

7. *A common solar pump system uses a 3 phase inverter to drive a variable frequency pump from a high voltage PV array. Water is pumped during daylight hours and stored in a large tank to supply periods without sunlight.*

8. *1 to 5kW domestic roof-mounted PV systems can be linked to the grid via a synchronised inverter. Surplus power in daylight is exported to the grid, whilst at night time energy is imported, removing the need for batteries*

System configurations
As we have seen, choices have to be made about what form of electricity the system will supply, whether it will need storage and what sources will provide the energy. There are many different ways to put the system together depending on what is required and what is available. Some of the more common system configurations are shown overleaf (Figure 2.2).

What will it cost?
There is a common misconception that renewable energy is 'free'. Indeed, the source of the energy or 'fuel' is free, as borne out by the low operation costs shown in the table below. However, the equipment to extract the energy, store it and convert it to a useful form is expensive.

Capital and recurrent costs
Once you have developed an initial design for your system, you will need to check that it fits within your budget. Renewable energy systems involve a high initial capital investment and low recurrent costs. Obviously, the capital cost will be the initial concern – can you afford the equipment and services required to set up the system? How do different systems and load regimes affect the costs?

Although there are no fuel costs to worry about (except for diesel-hybrid systems) there can be significant recurrent costs required to keep your system running. Battery replacement is the main recurrent expense, so the design life of the batteries relative to that of the entire system will have a big effect on future outlay. Figure 2.3 gives an idea of the division of costs in typical systems.

Life-cycle cost
To get an idea of how much expense you are letting yourself in for, and how different system configurations compare, it is useful to calculate the entire cost of the system over its life – the life-cycle cost. A key decision in the financial evaluation is to how long you expect the system to last before most of it needs replacing. A common figure in commercial RE applications is 20 years. Decent crystalline PV modules are guaranteed for 10 to 20 years, and good quality controllers and inverters should last this long if correctly sized and not mistreated too severely. Wind turbine life is highly

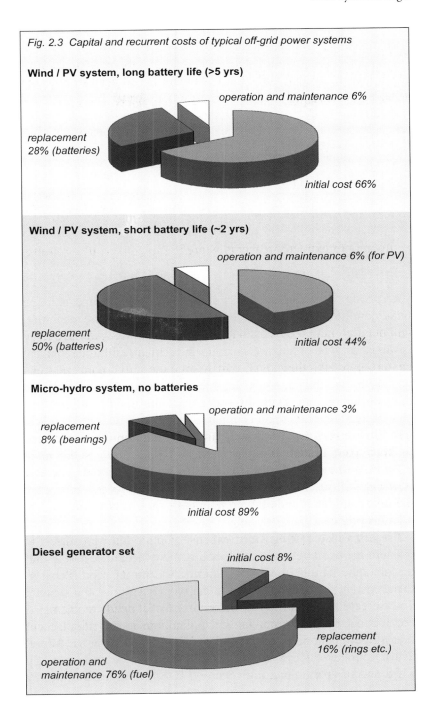

Fig. 2.3 Capital and recurrent costs of typical off-grid power systems

Wind / PV system, long battery life (>5 yrs)

operation and maintenance 6%

replacement
28% (batteries)

initial cost 66%

Wind / PV system, short battery life (~2 yrs)

operation and maintenance 6% (for PV)

replacement
50% (batteries)

initial cost 44%

Micro-hydro system, no batteries

operation and maintenance 3%

replacement
8% (bearings)

initial cost 89%

Diesel generator set

initial cost 8%

replacement
16% (rings etc.)

operation and
maintenance 76% (fuel)

Costing your system

Always be sure you have costed everything you need.
A typical list will include;
• Renewable energy generator(s) – PV, wind turbine, hydro, etc.
• Batteries
• Control systems – charge regulators, low voltage disconnect
• Monitoring – meters
• Support structures
• Inverters
• Cables
• Earthing system
• Fuse and distribution boxes
• Earth leakage protection
• Replacement of batteries after 5 to 10 years
• Delivery
• Installation

---

site-specific – turbulence (as occurs near obstacles) and extreme wind conditions take their toll on even the most robust machines, and regular maintenance and inspection is vital – failure of a rusting guy wire or seizure of an un-lubricated furling mechanism can prove catastrophic.

Batteries are the main consumable components. From the design daily discharge and cycle-life data from the manufacturers, you should be able to make an estimate of roughly how long they will last. Obviously, changes in loading from those initially envisaged will adversely affect battery life.

Hydro systems can last many decades, but turbine and generator bearings will need replacement every five to ten years. If you are using second-hand and DIY components, their useful life may be significantly less than 20 years.

Present value and discount rate

There are two approaches to totalling the expected cost of an RE system. The simple approach is to add the initial capital cost to the recurrent costs expected over the working life of the system. The second approach gives a more realistic estimate by using the accounting concept of present value. The idea behind this is that money spent now is worth more than that spent in the future. Thus, £100 invested in a savings account today could be worth £130 in five years' time; conversely, £100 in five years would be worth about £78 today. If the ensuing financial calculations appear too terrifying, skip over the equations but take note of the overall figures as they categorically demolish the common misconception that renewable energy is 'free'.

Life-cycle costing of a small wind/PV system			
Design life			20 years
Real discount rate			5%
Av. daily output			0.7kWh
Captial costs			
PV modules			£500
Wind turbine			£350
Batteries			£400
Controllers			£150
Wiring, mounting			£150
Installation			£150
Total capital cost			**£1700**
Future costs			
Year	Maintenance	Replace	Present Value
2	£20		£18
4	£20	£400	£346
6	£20		£15
8	£20	£400	£284
10	£20		£12
12	£20	£400	£234
14	£20		£10
16	£20	£400	£192
18	£20		£8
Totals	**£180**	**£1600**	**£1120**
Present value of future costs			£1120
Total cost			£1700
Total life-cycle cost			**£2820**

To calculate the present value of future costs, we use a 'discount rate', which can be seen as the rate of interest that would be earned if the money was invested rather than spent. To allow for the effects of inflation, an adjustment is made to obtain the 'real discount rate':

real discount rate = investment interest rate - inflation rate

A standard figure is 5%, but this could be adjusted to suit individual circumstances and non-financial benefits.

Life-cycle costs can be calculated by hand with a calculator or accounting tables, or using a spreadsheet programme. The formula is:

$P = C \times \{1 \div (1 + d)\}n$

where P is the present value of cost, C, in n years' time at discount rate d

Further adjustments can be made for escalation of costs beyond the rate of inflation, e.g. for fossil fuels, and also for repayment of loans used to raise the initial capital. Refer to an accounts textbook for further details.

Unit energy cost

Life-cycle costs can be used to compare similar systems with the same design life. However, the best way to compare the economics of different system designs and supply options is to use the life-cycle cost to find the cost per unit of energy (usually kWh, as used by grid electricity supply companies). This is achieved by amortising the total cost into equal annual amounts using the real interest rate (usually taken as equal to the real discount rate). This annual payment is then divided by the estimated annual energy production to arrive at an average cost of a unit of energy over the life of the system:

$$PA = CL \; \frac{(1 + i) . L . i}{(1 + i) . L - 1}$$

where PA is the annual payment on a system with a life-cycle cost, CL, and life time L years with a real interest rate, i, usually taken to be the same as the discount rate. If the system produces on average ED energy per day (kWh) then the unit energy cost, CU will be given by

$CU = PA \div (ED \times 365)$

Thus, considering our example above,

Annual payment, PA = 2820 x {(1 + 0.05)20 x 0.05}
÷ {(1 + 0.05)20 – 1} = £ 226

Cost per unit, CU = 226÷ (0.7 x 365) = £ 0.88 / kWh

This contrasts with the current UK unit price for grid electricity of about 11p / kWh and appears very expensive by comparison. In fact, this is a fairly typical unit price for a small RE system, illustrating the fact that making your own power on a small scale is usually eight to thirty times as expensive as buying it from companies that 'mass produce' it in large centralised power stations with many hidden subsidies. However, the total investment is significantly less than a grid connection fee, even where power lines are nearby. To make a fair comparison for an off-grid site, the connection fee would have to be included as part of the capital cost of the grid option.

Legal Considerations

Planning permission

Whatever kind of system you are planning, it is important to contact the Planning Department of your Local Authority in order to find out whether permission is required. It will apply to most wind and water power projects. The need to obtain permission for the siting of solar panels will depend on where you live. It will always be required in National Parks, SSSI's, AONB's and on listed buildings.

Building regulations

The only structures to which building regulations apply in this context are battery stores. Contact the Building Regulations Department of your Local Authority in order to find out what these are; when it is completed, someone will come and inspect your structure to confirm that it complies with the regulations.

Electrical safety

Your system will need to be checked by a certified electrician, who will issue you with a certificate if it is deemed statutorily safe under Part P of the building Regulations. If you have a grid-linked system you will already have been in discussions with the REC as regards the statutory requirements.

Hydro systems

Where a hydro system will divert a large proportion of a stream away from its natural course, the Environment Agency should be consulted for details of relevant regulations. They will consider the environmental impact of the scheme and, if acceptable, grant an abstraction licence. In general, the offtake should be designed so that some water continues to flow in the original course at all times. Fish ladders to allow the upstream passage of spawning fish past the offtake may also be required.

Chapter 3
Assessing Your Loads

Defining your loads

The equipment powered by a system is called its 'load'. The aim of your system is to produce as much electrical energy as your loads need. The more energy you need, the bigger and more expensive the system becomes, so it is worth checking to make sure you are using electricity efficiently. For example, low-energy light-bulbs can use as little as one seventh of the energy for the same light output as conventional tungsten bulbs.

Size your system to produce electricity for equipment that cannot be powered by any other means. This will keep your overall system cost down. In order to estimate what size system you will require you must first define exactly how much energy you need.

This chapter describes common loads such as heating, refrigeration, lighting and appliances, and then explains how to calculate your electrical energy requirements.

Types of loads

In most domestic situations, the main energy requirements are for water and space heating, cooking and refrigeration, and lighting. As already discussed, renewable electricity systems are not cost effective ways to supply heating loads. The exception to this rule is the case of larger hydro and wind based systems where excess power has to be 'dumped', water and space heating being the ideal means to do this.

Water heating Solar water heating panels can provide a cost effective source of hot water, especially when the bulk of demand is in the evening. The majority of conventional water heating systems waste significant amounts of energy keeping large tanks of water continually hot. A far more efficient system is to use a gas (bottled LPG) instantaneous heater, perhaps with a solar system pre-heating the supply. A back boiler arrangement in a solid fuel stove is also effective, especially in colder months when the stove would be in use for space heating. Locally produced firewood is a potentially renewable fuel (when trees are replanted) if somewhat labour-intensive.

Space heating The ideal situation would be to build your own house to a design incorporating passive solar heating and thermal efficiency features. Since this is rarely feasible, you should initially consider how to reduce the amount of heating required by using insulation, draught exclusion and other measures that reduce heat loss to the outside world. Wood stoves are a cheap and efficient way to heat space, and some will also provide hot water and cooking facilities.

Cooking Using an off-grid power system to power a cooker works out ten to twenty times as expensive as using primary energy sources such as wood and LPG. Gas is the ideal complement to a renewable energy system as it is efficient, clean and convenient. A wood stove precludes the need for a fossil fuel at the expense of extra labour and reduced convenience. The surplus heat generated is a bonus in winter but inconvenient in summer.

Refrigeration A common load in domestic systems is a fridge. It is not unusual for this to be the largest load on the system (see Case Studies 1 and 2) so careful selection and use can have a critical effect on system sizing. There are several different processes that can be used for cooling:

Evaporative coolers In warmer climes, people have used boxes made from chicken wire and charcoal to keep food cool. Water slowly percolates through the charcoal, absorbing heat as it evaporates. The body's sweat system uses the same principle, as do canvas water bags and unglazed earthenware water vessels. A good airflow around the container is essential for it to be effective.

Absorption fridges Many caravan equipment supplies stock absorption fridges that use LPG (bottled gas), 12V DC or 240V AC to provide heat that drives an absorption/evaporation/condensing cycle. These are fine for operating off a vehicle alternator or the mains, but are considerably less efficient than compressor fridges so are far from ideal for RE systems. If you do use one of these fridges, make sure there is provision for the considerable heat produced to escape. An advantage with these fridges is that they have no moving parts. However, they do not perform as well in hot climates.

AC compression fridges Conventional AC fridges use a vapour compression thermodynamic cycle to extract heat from the cabinet. They generally have minimal insulation (~25mm) so as to maximise internal volume for given exterior dimensions, but at the expense of operating efficiency. Since an inverter is required to run them, the inefficiencies are compounded. When starting, fridge compressors often briefly draw three to five times their running current, so make sure your inverter can cope with this short peak current. Use the smallest fridge that can meet your needs, and preferably with thick walls for improved insulation.

DC compression fridges These are quite expensive (several hundred pounds for a domestic model, and over a thousand for medical versions) but are by far the most efficient option. Insulation thickness tends to be 50 to 100mm, reducing energy requirements at the expense of extra bulk. Many models open from the top reducing the loss of cold air that occurs when the door is opened. Typical energy consumption is in the region of 3 watt-hours/litre/day. You may find that the extra cost for an inverter and the additional generating and storage capacity required to run a conventional fridge is more than the price of a new 12V fridge. Special medical fridges are available for use in vaccine cold-chains and blood banking. These have to meet stringent performance standards laid down by the World Health Organisation and are consequently very efficient and very expensive.

Improving refrigeration efficiency
- Set the thermostat as high as possible to reduce the cooling load.
- Let left-overs cool before placing in the fridge.
- Do not overfill as this restricts air movement, but keep it reasonably full to help store 'coolth'.
- Place the fridge in a cool, well ventilated part of the house.
- Do not open unnecessarily.
- Ensure the door seals properly.
- Defrost regularly.

A Dulas solar medical refrigerator, approved by the WHO for use in vaccine cold chains. The insulation in the walls is 100 mm thick and two separate 12V high efficiency compressors cool the vaccine chamber and a compartment for freezing ice-packs for use when distributing the vaccines.

12 Volt lighting In domestic off-grid systems, lighting is one of the most important loads. Since standard AC lights would require the use of an expensive and potentially inefficient inverter, it is often more sensible to use lights specifically designed for 12V DC supplies. Vehicles are an obvious source of bulbs, but these are usually incandescent tungsten filament bulbs which, though cheap, are inefficient and short-lived.

In addition to opting for efficient light sources, a large improvement in illumination can be achieved by the use of reflectors to direct the light to where it is needed, e.g. onto a desk rather than the ceiling. White painted surroundings also serve to maximise the illumination by reflection.

Halogen bulbs These are an incandescent light source consisting of a conducting filament in a bulb filled with a halogen gas. They produce about twice as much light and last twice as long as an equivalent tungsten bulb but are more expensive. Special automotive versions are available, but the most useful for domestic applications take the form of small bayonet or Edison screw bulbs that mount on standard fittings, or sealed spot and flood light units designed for 12V display lighting. The sealed beam-type is particularly useful for work desks and benches where strong, focused lighting is required. Typical examples cost £2 to £10 and consume 10 to 50 watts. They can be sensitive to changes in voltage, and this can be an issue on battery systems where the voltage can vary. Operating a 12V tungsten-halogen bulb at 12.6V can reduce its life expectancy by up to 50% (from 2000-1000 hours). Conversely, operating the bulb at 11.4V will double the life expectancy of the bulb.

Fluorescent lights These are highly efficient lights that create illumination using a high voltage electrical discharge through a glass tube filled with low pressure mercury vapour and argon gas. The mercury gives off ultra-violet light that causes the phosphor coating inside the tube to glow with a bright white light. They require fittings that include circuitry that starts and maintains the discharge, and produce about five times as much light as an equivalently powered tungsten filament bulb.

Many 240V AC fluorescent lights appear to have an annoying flicker as they are operating at mains frequency (50Hz); this is not a problem with 12V fittings as they use electronic ballast inverters that operate at much higher frequencies. The most common type are the small 'strip' lights available at caravan suppliers using one or two 8 to 15W tubes. An alternative is the compact 'PL'-type fluorescent with a tube bent into a 'U'-shape. These tend to be more expensive, but are also more efficient than many strip lights. The ballast inverters that maintain the discharge are sensitive to low voltages and tend to overheat or blacken the ends of the tubes when operated at less than 11.5V. Be careful to keep cable voltage drops as low as possible to prevent this (see Chapter 8). One or two 8W strip lights will comfortably illuminate a small room.

Light Emitting Diodes (LEDs) Light emitting diodes are small electronic components encased in coloured transparent plastic that emit low level light when small currents pass through them in a particular direction. They are found in numerous electrical devices, serving as illuminated indicators and displays. There is a wide variety available with varying colours (red, green, yellow and orange – blue and white ones are also available but are more expensive) and visibility from wide-angle to focussed beams. They are cheap and efficient, consuming a few hundredths of a watt, with operating currents of 5 to 30mA at 2.1V, and typically costing a few pence each. Grouped together in clusters, LEDs can provide a source of directed bright focussed illumination e.g. for work surfaces, or low-level illumination, e.g. for controls or as a nightlight. Connected into long strings they can be used for a decorative 'fairy light' effect or for marking paths and entrances.

RE suppliers are beginning to stock commercial LED 'bulbs' consisting of several high power LEDs in a standard fitting for use in 12 volt systems. These provide low-level lighting using less than 1 watt. Again, they are very sensitive to over voltage, and care must be taken if constructing home-made LED lights to allow for voltage fluctuations.

Low voltage DC appliances An increasing range of electrical equipment is now available which will run directly from 12 or 24 volts DC. Although primarily designed for the trucking or marine market these items will function perfectly well in a domestic RE system. As some equipment is designed for 12 volts and some for 24 volts it is always important to ensure that the voltage is correct for your system. Using DC directly from the batteries will remove the financial cost and power losses associated with an inverter, with the added advantage that low voltage DC is inherently safer. But, as with any electrical appliance, it is important to ensure it contains a fuse of the correct value. If in doubt contact your retailer. Low voltage DC equipment can be bought from marine, trucking and motor home suppliers and from RE system suppliers.

The single PV module mounted on this house in rural Zimbabwe supplies power for lights, TV and a record player.

Wiring up 12V LED strings

It is simple to connect LEDs so that they will operate on a 12V supply. A proven method is to connect five LEDs of the same current rating in series, along with a small resistor to limit current and drop the remaining volts (see below). It is important to check the polarity of the diodes so that they are connected positive to negative all along the string. The negative terminal is generally shorter than the positive, and on the lip of round LEDs there is a flat section on the negative side. Encase the connected LEDs in a transparent tube, or simply cover the bare connections with tape, heat shrink or hot glue. Long strings or clusters of 'fairy lights' can be made by connecting in parallel many sections of five LEDs and resistor onto two long positive and negative wires. Twist the wires together using a drill, untwisting a bit at the end to stop it kinking. As the currents involved are so low, thin wire such as 0.5mm² is adequate.

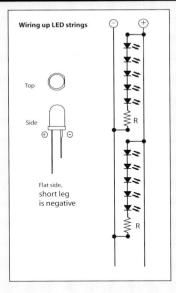

Wiring up LED strings

Top

Side

Flat side, short leg is negative

Voltage drop over LED	= 2.1V
Voltage drop over 5 LED's	= 10.5V
Nominal supply voltage	= 12.0V
=> Voltage over series resistor, R, VR	= 1.5V
Ohm's Law states R	= V / I
Thus, for 5 mA LED's R	= 1.5 / 0.005 = 300Ω
For 10 mA LED's R	= 150Ω
For 20 mA LED's R	= 75Ω

Assessing your loads

The most convenient energy unit for measuring loads is the watt-hour. Ten watt-hours are ten watts used for one hour or 2 watts used for five hours; it's that simple!

If you are using power every day you will need to work out your daily average consumption.

Estimating your average daily load:

i) Use energy-efficient appliances (such as low-energy light bulbs) wherever possible.

ii) Make separate lists of the AC and DC appliances you wish to use, and consider which are essential and which are merely desirable.

iii) Find the power rating of each piece of equipment (in watts), either from the maker's name plate on the back of the appliance, or consulting the power consumption table given below.

iv) Estimate the average number of hours each appliance will be used each day.

v) Calculate the number of watt-hours each appliance consumes (watts from the power rating x hours in use).

vi) Multiply the AC watt-hours by around 1.2 to allow for inverter inefficiencies, depending on the inverter you choose (see Chapter 6 – Inverters).

The total gives you a fair idea of how much energy (watt-hours) you will need on average to keep you going for a day. There is a worked example shown opposite, and further examples in the Case Studies to help you with these calculations.

AC loads

It is worth adding up the power rating of each appliance to find the maximum number of watts you will be using if everything is switched on at once. If there is any likelihood of this occurring, the inverter or hydro-generator should be sized to cope with this.

Certain loads such as fridge compressors, motors and fluorescent lights require as much as three times their operating power for brief periods when starting. Look for an inverter that can provide more than its rated output for short periods to cope with these start-up peaks.

More information about running AC loads from inverters is provided in Chapter 6.

Variations in loads

Daily: Many appliances, such as refrigerators, are in operation for 24 hours per day but do not run continuously. They have a thermostat that will turn them on and off as required to keep their internal temperature constant. To get an approximate idea of the proportion of the day they are actually running for it is possible to record the run time over a few hours with a stopwatch, but bear in mind the run time will be greatest when the room temperature is highest, (so keep your fridge in a cool place!).

Weekly: Some loads may only be required on a weekly basis, e.g. spin dryer, sewing machine, power tools. Estimate the total use over a week and then divide by 7 for an average daily load.

Load Assessment Table

	LOADS		Power watts	TIME	ENERGY
Appliance	AC/DC	Number in use		Hours of use per day	Total energy consumed Wh/day
1 Light	DC	1	12W	x 3	= 36Wh
2 Light	DC	1	8W	x 3	= 24Wh
3 Stereo	DC	1	20W	x 4	= 80Wh
4 **Total dc load load** (rows 1+2+3)					**140Wh**
5 Sewing machine	AC	1	60W	x 0.5	= 30Wh
6 Television	AC	1	60W	x 2	= 120Wh
7 Video	AC	1	40W	x 1	= 40Wh
8			Peak load **160W**	Total AC load (rows 5+6+7) **190Wh**	
9 Allowance for inverter loss (approx. 20% of load)				38Wh	= 8 x 20%
10 Total inverter load				228Wh	= 8 + 9
11 **Total DC consumption**				**368Wh**	= 4 + 10
12 Allowances for battery losses (approx. 25% of load)				92Wh	= 11 x 25%
13 **Input energy to battery required per day**				**460Wh**	= 11 + 12

Battery sizing

14 Days of reserve	5 days		
15 Max depth of discharge	60%		
16 Capacity required		3833Wh	= 13 x 14/15
17 At system voltage	12V	319Ah	= 16/voltage
18 Average daily discharge	12%		= 13/16

Seasonal: Many loads vary seasonally throughout the year. Refrigerators will work much harder in the summer, whilst more lighting will be needed during the longer winter nights. If these variable loads form a significant part of the total, it is best to calculate separate daily average loads for summer and winter, or even on a month by month basis. Compare the loads to the energy available during that period – the point where load divided by resource is highest will dictate your required generating capacity. Solar PV is best suited to summer peak loads, but panels can be orientated with a higher tilt angle to maximise input during winter months when the sun is lower in the sky. In temperate climates, wind and hydro generally produce more energy in the winter.

Priorities and flexibility

When calculating expected consumption, use higher estimates for critical loads, and lower ones for optional loads. One approach is to multiply estimated loads by a 'priority factor', for example, 1.25 for critical loads, 1.0 for essential, and 0.75 for optional loads. The larger the factor, the greater the confidence you can have in continued supply.

Certain loads can be adjusted to suit the available energy – use lower estimates for these flexible loads.

Future expansion

As previously mentioned, it is expensive to oversize a system. However, in many domestic applications, it is likely that loads will increase as families expand or extra appliances are added. PV systems are quite modular, and can be enlarged by simply adding more panels. Wind systems require extra towers and turbines if space is available. Hydro-generators are much harder to expand.

Adding extra batteries to an existing system is far from ideal, so it may be worth considering system expansion in a series of phases linked to the replacement time of the battery bank.

Where expansion is likely, it may be worth slightly over-sizing 'balance of system' components such as controllers, cables and meters. For instance, if you can only afford one 50Wp PV now, but want to add another next year, consider a 10 amp rather than 5 amp controller.

Power consumption table

Device	Supply	Power
Halogen light	DC, 12/24V	5–20W
Fluorescent light	DC, 12/24V AC	8–20W 11W–40W
Fridge 225 litre 100 litre	AC AC	150–300W; 2–5kWh/day 100–200W; 1–2kWh/day
Fridge (100 litre)	DC, 12V, 24V	30–60W; 0.2-0.6kWh/day
TV, colour, new	AC	40–120W
TV, colour	DC, 12V	60W
TV, B&W	DC, 12V	10–20W
Music system	AC	30–50W
Portable stereo	DC, 6–12V	5–20W
VCR	AC	10–40W
Computer, desktop	AC	100–250W
Computer, laptop/ notebook	DC, 9–18V	10–30W
Printer, inkjet	DC/AC	15–50W, 2–6W standby
Printer, laser	AC	500–900W
Fax machine	AC	40–80W, 2–6W standby
Photocopier	AC	50W (idle), 700–1500W (operating)
Sewing machine	AC	50–80W
Blender, mixer	AC	100–300W
Vacuum cleaner	AC	500–1500W
Iron	AC	500–1500W
Washing machine	AC	300–800W (cold) 1500–3000W (hot)
VHF/UHV radio	DC, 12/24V	1–10W (standby) 25–80W (transmit)

NB. Most appliances carry a plate or stamp detailing operating voltages and power consumption.

Typical power consumption

General principles
Don't overestimate
Costs for wind and solar systems tend to rise proportionally with design load so overestimation of your load can result in expensive over-capacity.

Prioritise loads
Rank your different loads according to their importance. By dividing loads into categories such as critical, essential and preferable you can compare the costs of basic and comprehensive systems (see Case Study 2).

Consider alternative appliances
Consider what equipment can be used to achieve the desired results, e.g. AC, DC or gas powered fridges, or evaporative cooler.

Use suitable energy sources
Choose energy sources that match the load. For heating loads, use primary sources such as solar water-heating panels, wood stoves and gas cookers. What loads can only be powered by electricity? For short term or occasional heavy loads such as welding machines and pumps, consider petrol and diesel-powered generators.

Chapter 4
Generating Power

How much electricity can you generate?

Once you have calculated how much electricity you require, you need to look at how much you can generate. How far it is worth making actual site measurements of the resource to make this assessment varies widely, depending on the scope and budget of the project.

In small systems, which may range down to less than 100 watts, the cost of even a modest degree of monitoring could easily exceed the cost of the energy system itself. However, some form of low cost site assessment (perhaps just relying on available meteorological data) and performance monitoring is still desirable even if at this scale it involves only manual 'spot' measurements. Domestic or institutional scale systems can often benefit from a continuous monitoring system, perhaps with a mimic panel display as a means of educating users and others about the system, and helping them to make the best use of it. If you do attempt your own resource measurement, remember:

Resource measuring equipment usually has to operate in a hostile physical environment; windy hilltops with horizontal rain and the occasional lightning strike, the extreme heat of some windless PV sites, sandstorms, or flood-prone river valleys may well render much electronic equipment useless before an adequate amount of data has been collected!

The resource data must be collected over fairly long periods, several months at least, and preferably much longer, in order to be meaningful. This has implications for the amount of data that must be stored by monitoring systems, and thought should be given to some pre-processing of the data (e.g. storing daily averages and peaks, etc., rather than all the measured data). Other important points are long-term reliability of equipment, how data is collected for analysis and the frequency of site visits required.

Many RE sites have no grid electricity available to power monitoring equipment, so for resource assessment a small independent PV system is often used. Low power consumption and the ability to recover gracefully from power outages are important factors in choosing equipment.

In the UK and many other parts of the world, long term data may be available from a local meteorological station, or, for rivers, a hydrological survey site. Short term data from your site may be compared to this data to find a correlation relationship which can be used to estimate your resource over long periods.

Below, we consider the basics of how to assess different energy sources, and list some simple formulae that will help you estimate how much power is available.

Photovoltaics

In Britain, the low light levels encountered during the winter means that PV panels are often used as part of a hybrid energy system (i.e. in conjunction with other generators).

Photovoltaic panel manufacturers describe their products in terms of their rated output. You will hear people talking about 50 watt panels or, more precisely, 50 watt peak (Wp) panels. This refers to their maximum power output under peak sun at 25°C. Under real conditions with the panel at higher temperature (typically 40 to 60°C), output will be 80% to 90% of this peak value. In order to work out the amount of energy (in watt-hours) generated in a day, you need to know the daily average energy from the sun in your part of the world. This can be obtained from 'insolation maps' like Fig. 3.1. Such data is readily available throughout Europe and many other parts of the world and is often presented as monthly means or hour-of-the-day means for each month (see Resources). The easiest insolation maps to use give you the number of 'peak' sunshine hours equivalent to the total amount received over the whole of a typical day. If you multiply this figure by the peak output rating of the panel, you will get a figure (in watt-hours) for daily energy production. A different map can be used for each of the four seasons, and sometimes for each month.

You must check that your site does not get too badly shaded at times of the year or day, which you can do by observation and

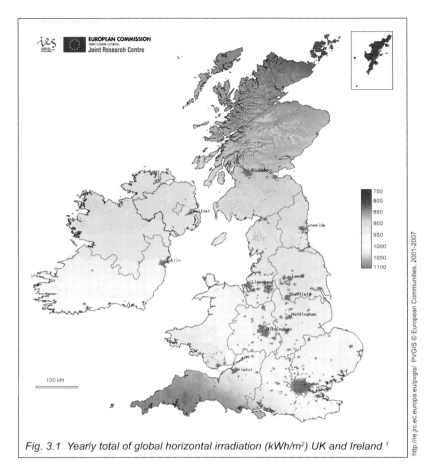

Fig. 3.1 Yearly total of global horizontal irradiation (kWh/m²) UK and Ireland [1]

common sense.

Solar radiation variations are much less localised than wind energy, so there is less need for direct measurements provided that reasonably local data is available.

In combination with the information about different panels, (see Resources), you will then be able to construct graphs showing average seasonal power outputs from different sized arrays. You will then be able to assess to what extent the available solar resource matches your needs at different times of the year (see the worked example in Case Study 2).

There are also several online calculator systems to help you estimate the output of the system. Two free online resources are:

- RETSCREEN – a spreadsheet based programme that helps to assess system size, cost and output. Free to download from http://www.retscreen.net
- PVGIS – a web based system to estimate annual irradiation and also has a PV generation estimator. Uses grid references and a GIS database. (Hint: set PV losses to 20% for more accurate results) http://re.jrc.ec.europa.eu/pvgis/apps/pvest. php?lang=en&map=europe

Most people buy what they can afford – the cost of measuring solar radiation may be as high as the equipment, so it's better to get one or two extra panels instead.

Measuring solar radiation If you do want to measure the amount of solar radiation yourself, here are three methods, ranging from professional to budget approaches.

Professionally, solar radiation is usually measured with a pyranometer. This consists of a black radiation absorber and a shiny or white radiation reflector equipped with sensors to measure the temperature difference between the two. Double glass hemispheres are added to reduce the effects of wind and convection. The electrical output is an analogue DC voltage of around 10mV. As it is rather small, it must be treated carefully to avoid adding electrical noise and drift errors.

A cheaper alternative is to use a PV cell and to measure its short-circuit current. The PV cell has non-ideal angular and wavelength responses, which can, however, be improved by the addition of optical filters; temperature correction is also needed to get the best accuracy. Calibrated PV cell sensors cost about a third of the cost of pyranometers.

For a really cheap solution, an ordinary PV cell may be used and calibrated by assuming that summer clear sky mid-day radiation is $1000W/m^2$.

When measuring solar radiation yourself, a tilted sensor can be used if you know the tilt angle you are going to use. Otherwise, to estimate the radiation falling on any tilted surface, both the direct radiation and the diffuse radiation falling on the horizontal plane should be measured. A number of instruments are available to do this, mostly using one sensor with a shadow band (to block the direct component) or using a collimated sensor mounted on a sun-tracker to measure only the direct component while another sensor measures both direct and diffuse radiation.

Windpower

To estimate the average output from a wind turbine you will need to find out the average windspeed at your site. Approximate information on the average windspeeds for your area is becoming increasingly available from the Meteorological Office (see Resources), or, for free, from the online NOABL windspeed calculator, when you give a LandRanger grid reference for the kilometre square in which the site is located. The website can give windspeed estimates at three heights: 10m, 25m or 45m above ground at the site, and also in each of the eight adjoining squares. Local conditions will also have an effect, and you should make allowances for shelter from trees, etc.

Alternatively, you can measure the wind with a cup anemometer and log the wind-speed over a period of a year or so. Mechanical and electrical cup-counter anemometers are also available; these measure run-of-wind and periodic readings allow the mean windspeed to be calculated. Electrical anemometers usually produce pulse outputs using a reed switch or optical sensor where each pulse represents length of wind-run. They are not prohibitively expensive and may be a worthwhile investment.

A cup anemometer and wind speed data logger.

The instantaneous power in the wind depends on the cube of the windspeed, so mean windspeed does not tell the whole story. To estimate the energy available a 'wind pattern factor' based on wind statistics for similar sites must be used to estimate the long-term mean of v3 given the measure of mean windspeed (v). Alternatively, an electronic wind-logger may be used to record from the anemometer. This data can then be correlated to long term meteorological data and a fair estimation of average windspeed calculated. In most domestic-sized systems this process could cost more than the wind turbine itself!

Once the average windspeed has been determined, the energy content of the wind can then be worked out. The corresponding energy output of the machine can be found from the annual energy output/average windspeed graphs supplied by wind turbine manufacturers. See the example in Case Study 2. For a rough estimate you can use the formula given on page 54.

For more information refer to *Choosing Windpower* (see Resources) where you will find details of common machines, and a computer algorithm that you can use in conjunction with your data and that from the turbine manufacturer.

Water power

There are several ways of estimating the flow in your stream or river. You may construct a dam with a notch in it. This makes the depth of water flowing through the notch (which you can easily measure) vary with the volume of water per second through the notch, allowing you to calculate the volume of flow over a period of time. You will need to measure this throughout the year, to assess seasonal variations.

Rainfall figures for the catchment area of your watercourse are a common source of information, with a percentage deducted for evaporation and other losses. The National River Authority publishes run-off data for most areas, with allowances for the seasonal flow rate, as a rainfall unit for the catchment area.

The equations in the box on page 54 will then give you the available power. The 'head' is the vertical distance from the water intake to the turbine wheel. Multiplying this by your flow and the gravitational constant gives you the power in kilowatts, with a correction factor to account for efficiency losses. For more information see the companion CAT publications *Micro-Hydro Power Factsheet, Going with the Flow* (see Resources) and Case Study 1.

Measuring the flow of a stream with a dam made from plastic sheeting and a piece of wood with a 'V' shaped notch. (J Randle)

Estimating available power by source

Solar Power

The energy produced per PV panel in a day is given by the following simple formula:

Energy generated =
        panel rated output x   peak sunshine hours x   0.85
          (watt-hours/day)   (watts)   (hours/day)

Windpower

There is a 'rule of thumb' which you can use for rough estimates:

$$Paverage = \frac{(P10m/s \times Vmean - 2.5)}{9.5}$$

Paverage = the average power output estimate in watts.
P10m/s = power output of the turbine at a windspeed of 10m/s.
This may be less than the manufacturer's rated power.
Vmean = average windspeed for the site in metres per second.

Note that this formula becomes very inaccurate below 3.5m/sec and above 7m/sec average windspeed. Also that although the instantaneous power in the wind goes up as the cube of the speed, the average power from a wind turbine does not. Away from very low or very high wind speeds the average power output of a typical small turbine varies almost linearly with the mean windspeed because of the way that the wind statistics and the shape of a machine's power curve interact. The formula also fails for machines with unusually shaped power/speed curves and for some wind regimes (it is based on typical UK patterns).

Daily energy output = Paverage x 24
(watt-hours/day)   (watts)

Water Power

A hydro scheme requires both water flow and a drop in height (referred to as 'head') to produce useful power. No energy conversion system is 100% efficient, so assuming a conversion efficiency of around 50% a good estimate of the net power output of such a system is given by:

Net power	=	50% x head	x	flow rate	x	g
(W)		(metres)		(litres / sec)		(m/s²)

≈ 5 x head x flow rate

Where the flow is sufficient that the turbine can run all day at full power;

Daily energy output (kWh) = 24(hrs) x net power (kW)

Engine powered generators

Although this book is primarily concerned with renewable power sources, there are sometimes situations where the occasional use of an engine generator can be cost effective. This is particularly applicable where an engine-based system is already in place. Systems combining diesel and renewable sources are often known as diesel-hybrids. Such systems are usually AC-based and use the generator to cover peak loads and charge a battery bank that feeds an inverter to provide power for general loading. The renewable sources feed the battery via a controller. Case Study 3 describes such a system that was installed in a remote Zimbabwean school.

The addition of batteries, an inverter-charger and other power sources can reduce generator use by 80% or more, greatly increasing the generator's life and reducing fuel costs. Obviously, this extra equipment adds significant capital expense in exchange for the saving in recurrent costs. A good indicator of whether such a system will be cost effective is to assess the capacity factor of the generator-only system. This is the fraction of actual loads to the rated output and can be calculated by dividing the average load (in kilowatts) over, say, a day, by the rated kilowatt output. Capacity factors of 0.25 make it worthwhile considering the addition of batteries. Situations where diesel-hybrid systems may be viable include:

• Existing off-grid supplies using diesel generators
• Load regimes that include high power appliances such as welders, machine tools and large domestic loads such as washing machines
• Critical applications where the battery bank or power supply from renewable sources necessary to meet all eventualities would make the system unfeasibly expensive
• Mobile systems that have access to engine powered alternators

How much power will you need to generate?

Before deciding which generator to buy you must estimate how much energy you need to produce. You will know this figure from your calculation of average daily loads. However, for systems using batteries, a multiplier of around 1.25 is required to make up for the fact that batteries lose, on average, around 20% of the energy they store. In addition there may be other inefficiencies that may require a further increase in the generator size; see later sections for this. So, the formula is:

Average daily generated output = 1.25 x average daily energy requirement

For worked examples of this calculation see the Case Studies.

The secret of a successful system is to generate sufficient energy so that the average output at your site meets your needs, either on a daily, weekly or monthly basis. If continuity of supply is essential, or if you will be using appliances with surges in their power demand such as washing machines or photocopiers, you may choose to install a diesel generator or other form of hybrid system, such as wind/PV, wind/diesel, or PV/wind.

Don't overestimate

Since the costs of most RE-based systems rise more-or-less proportionally with size, an over-sized system can seriously affect the cost effectiveness of the system. Big savings can be made by considering how good load management can be incorporated into the load assessment to reduce the system size.

[1]Šúri M., Huld T.A., Dunlop E.D. Ossenbrink H.A., 2007. Potential of solar electricity generation in the European Union member states and candidate countries. Solar Energy (in press), http://re.jrc.ec.europa.eu/pvgis/

Chapter 5
Storing Your Electricity Using Batteries

Batteries are the heart of many off-grid systems, storing and releasing energy to match your power supply to your demand. Solar photovoltaic panels generate power during daylight hours, but lights are required after dark. Wind turbines can generate continuously during windy periods, but produce nothing during calm weather. Batteries store power as it is generated, releasing it to run loads when demand is greater than the generated supply. They act like a fuel tank or bank account for the RE system.

Unfortunately, batteries are expensive, hazardous and have a limited lifespan. Their periodic replacement is the main recurrent cost in renewable energy systems. In Chapter 2, we considered how to avoid them, either by grid connection or directly generating regulated 230V AC. However, if you must have batteries, then understanding them and their needs will you help get the best from them.

Batteries store low voltage (2, 6, 12, or 24 volts) DC electricity. This is different from the 240V AC from grid supplies or diesel generators. Batteries are, in many ways, the most vulnerable part of your system. Using a system with damaged batteries is inefficient, as much of your precious electricity is being wasted. But with proper care and understanding your batteries will give good service.

Most off-grid renewable energy systems use lead-acid batteries for energy storage. They are far from the 'ideal' storage battery, but are the best of a bad lot! The only other serious option is to use nickel-cadmium batteries; these do have some advantages (particularly their ability to tolerate being left fully discharged without permanent damage), but they are much more expensive and have a higher environmental impact than lead-acid batteries. For very small portable systems such as solar lanterns, etc. it might be worth considering one of the newer batteries such as nickel-hydride or lithium ion batteries which offer reduced size, weight and environmental cost compared to nickel-cadmium. These are often found in notebook computers and mobile phones, but at present are far too expensive for a domestic-scale system.

Battery Capacity

The capacity of a battery (units: amp-hours – Ah) is a measure of how much electrical energy the battery can store. A 100 amp-hour battery will theoretically supply 1 amp for 100 hours or 10 amps for 10 hours. If batteries are connected together in parallel (positive to positive and negative to negative) their voltage will remain the same but their capacity will increase. This should normally only be done with batteries of the same type and capacity.

The battery capacity in amp-hours multiplied by the terminal voltage gives its energy storage capacity in watt-hours. For example, a 100Ah, 12V battery stores

100Ah x 12V = 1200Wh (because W = V x A)

So a battery with a capacity of 1.2kWh has enough juice in it to run a 100W light bulb for 12 hours.

In reality, using all the energy stored in a battery will damage it, and the usable capacity varies with how much current is delivered. Discharging a battery at a low current can yield as much as 20% more energy than at a high current. In order to clarify this, battery manufacturers usually quote a discharge rate to achieve a specified capacity. Charging or discharging rates are often expressed as C/10, C/20, C/100, etc., where C is the amp-hour capacity (sometimes called the ampacity) and C/10, for instance, means a current that will empty (or fill) the battery in 10 hours. Thus, a battery may be nominally rated 100 amp-hours for discharge at C/20 or a '20 hour rate' (i.e. 100 / 20 = 5 amps) but may deliver 110 amp-hours at C/100 (1.1 amps) or 90 amp-hours at C/5 (18 amps). Since the load currents in most off-grid systems tend to be very variable, and are rarely high for long periods, it is usual to use the nominal capacity for design calculations.

Sizing battery banks

Choosing how many batteries you will need requires a compromise between cost and reliability. To estimate the required capacity of your battery store, multiply your average daily load by the number of days reserve you require. The actual battery size you need may be as much as twice this figure, as you should only discharge your batteries to between 50% to 80% of their total capacity to get the best life out of them before they need replacing.

The choice of how many days reserve you need depends on the reliability of your energy source, the nature of the load and how deeply you intend to discharge your batteries.

Availability of energy sources

By their very nature, most renewable energy sources depend on the weather. Successful system design relies on an understanding of both seasonal and daily variations. Given the variability of the British climate, a reasonable wind turbine site is unlikely to get becalmed for more than a day or two, whilst bright sunny days may not appear for a week or more, especially in winter. Hydro systems are more site specific, depending on the catchment area and its ability to store and gradually release the rain it has received (a natural battery effect). In the UK flows are generally lower in the summer, and may stop completely on some sites during long periods without rain. Your reserve capacity should cover you for the longest period that you reasonably expect to be without power input.

The accuracy of your resource estimation also affects your choice of storage capacity. If you are uncertain of the energy available, it is wise to increase your days of reserve, or alternatively expand your generating ability (or reduce loading).

By combining sources in a hybrid system you can greatly reduce the chances of receiving no energy for more than a day or two, since dry, calm and cloudy days do not occur very often. If your system includes a generator, perhaps to supply a heavy load such as a welder, you can use it for occasional charging during slack periods, thus further reducing your need for storage capacity.

Load types

In typical domestic systems, a few days a year with no power are a minor inconvenience. Once you have lived with your system for a while you will know when to economise on use to eke out your remaining amp hours during low power periods.

In many non-domestic applications, reliability of supply is far more important. Loss of power for a telecommunications or data gathering installation can prove very expensive, and for signalling or medical applications it could prove life-threatening. In such cases, the extra cost of batteries to cover a week or more is justified by the need for reliability. Such systems usually require more sophisticated design techniques than those outlined here; computer software is available to optimise reliability and cost-effectiveness. These packages often work by creating an algebraic model of the system and then feeding it with typical meteorological and loading data to simulate its behaviour and calculate the 'loss of power probability' – the chances of a black-out. Simple versions can be written using standard spreadsheet packages.

Larger systems often use a multiple low-voltage disconnection system where low priority loads are automatically shed long before the more critical loads. In smaller systems, the user will learn to do this manually.

Reserve days

Priority	Typical load	Reserve
Low	Ornamental, occasional use	1-3 days
Medium	Domestic	3-6 days
High	Telecoms, data capture	5-8 days
Critical	Medical refrigeration	7-10 days

These figures are purely indicators of typical system designs and should not be regarded as definitive. In general, variety of sources and flexibility of loading reduces the battery storage required.

Depth of discharge

Deep-cycle batteries are designed to regularly discharge between 30% and 80% of their capacity. Deeper discharging reduces the lifetime of the battery as demonstrated by the table below.

When deciding on battery capacity, you should consider both the expected daily depth of discharge (DoD), and the maximum allowable discharge. An approximate indication of the first is given

Depth of Discharge	'Leisure' battery life	Vented deep-cycle battery life
10%	750 cycles	5300 cycles
50%	310 cycles	1350 cycles
80%	200 cycles	900 cycles

by the daily load (in amp-hours) divided by the battery capacity. By comparing this percentage to cycle-life data for the battery you can calculate roughly how long the battery will last. Using the table above as an example, the leisure battery would need replacing after about 2 years with a daily DoD of 10%, whilst the deep-cycle battery could last as long as 4 years at 50% DoD.

If, as advised, you have a load controller, the maximum DoD is set by the voltage at which your over-discharge (low voltage disconnect) control activates; this dictates how often you are likely to lose power. Your battery bank should be big enough to store enough daily demand for the entire reserve period before reaching this level. If you expect this to occur more than once a month, revise your figures to allow more storage capacity.

Battery sizing table			
Expected daily load	L	380	watt-hours
Reserve capacity	R	5	days
Maximum DoD	M	50%	
=> Estimated capacity	$C = L \times R \div M$	3800	watt-hours
	At 12V, => C÷12	317	amp-hours
=> Approx Daily DoD	$D \approx L \div C$	10%	

The lead-acid battery

Lead-acid batteries have been in general use for over 80 years and are the most common type of rechargeable battery. In the battery, electrical energy is converted to chemical energy and stored as such until the battery is discharged, the chemical composition changes, and electrical energy is released again. This happens because of reactions between the battery's lead plates and a sulphuric acid solution, called the electrolyte.

A basic lead-acid cell has a terminal voltage of around 2 volts. A standard 12V battery contains six cells connected in series with internal link. Some larger batteries are supplied as 2 volt cells with external connections.

Lead-acid batteries (and Ni-Cads) come in both 'vented' types with a liquid electrolyte (like most car batteries) and removable cell caps, and in 'sealed' types, often with a gel electrolyte that cannot be topped-up. The 'vented' types are more common and cheaper for higher capacities, but need more maintenance.

All lead-acid batteries are based upon the same chemical reaction between dilute sulphuric acid and lead. These have, however, evolved into different types, which are best suited to different uses.

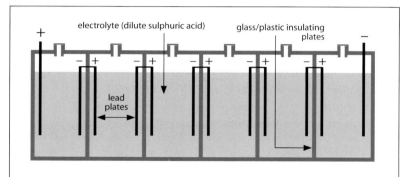

Fig. 5.1 A lead-acid battery is composed of a series of cells connected together. The nature of the chemical reaction involved results in the voltage on each cell being around 2V. The 2V cells can be connected together in series (positive to negative) to give the required voltage. i.e., six 2V cells connected in series give a 12V battery.

Automotive (SLI) Batteries

Designed for vehicle starting, lights and ignition (hence SLI), these batteries should be avoided if possible. They are specifically designed to give a short burst of high current to start a vehicle's engine and then be immediately recharged. Although the current drawn is quite high (around 300 amps) the amount of time it needs to flow before the vehicle starts and the battery is recharged is quite short (2 to 8 seconds on average) so the resulting depth of discharge is actually quite shallow.

To make vehicle batteries as cheaply as possible with the minimum weight they are constructed from a large number of thin plates or grids of 'lead sponge' to give the maximum surface area for the reaction to occur. This thin plate construction results in very poor performance if the batteries are discharged more deeply. Typically SLI batteries begin to fail after less than 100 cycles of 50% discharge, with complete failure after around 200 cycles.

'Leisure' Batteries

These have some of the characteristics of both the vehicle battery and the true deep cycle battery. In general, they have thicker plates and contain more electrolyte than SLI batteries. Some are available as 'low maintenance' or 'maintenance-free'. They are often advertised as deep cycle but do not have the same cycle life as true deep cycle batteries, being generally smaller and cheaper. They are often used in small solar home systems in developing countries and if looked after can manage 200 to 400 cycles to 40-50% discharge. If they are used for deep cycling (80% discharge) they will last a little better than vehicle batteries. Good quality Leisure and Deep cycle batteries have become almost interchangeable. If from new, the price can give a good indication of the quality of the battery

Deep Cycle Batteries

A true deep cycle lead-acid battery is designed to have up to 80% of its charge removed and repeatedly replaced 1000-2000 times over a period of 5 to 15 years. Such batteries are more expensive initially, but over their lifetime represent much better value for money per discharge cycle than leisure or SLI batteries. The plates or grids in a deep cycle battery are over four times thicker than those of a vehicle battery. Rather than sponge lead, they are generally made from scored sheets of lead alloy often containing up to 16% of the metal antimony. The antimony does not take part in the chemical reaction but provides strength and longer life to the plates. Traction batteries often use tubular electrodes to maximise surface area within the available volume.

In addition to the difference in the plates, deep cycle batteries are generally larger and more rugged, with a larger gap between the plates to prevent particles of lead which have become dislodged from causing micro short circuits. Deep cycle batteries are often constructed from individual cells that are externally connected together with thick metal straps to form a battery; this has the advantage that if one of the cells breaks down it can be replaced without replacing the whole battery. As with all batteries, proper cycling techniques, environment and sizing are essential to ensure maximum life.

A battery store comprised of 2V vented cells in use with a windpower system in Scotland.

Sealed 'VRLA' Deep Cycle Batteries

These come in two varieties with the acid electrolyte in the form of a liquid (as normal) or as a gel, suspended in an absorbent glass mat. The container is sealed, making these batteries ideal

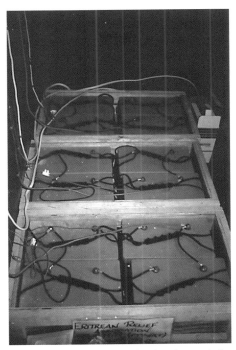

A bank of sealed gel batteries forming part of a medical refrigeration system in Eritrea.

for environments where acid vapours and spills are not acceptable. Such batteries are more strict in their charging and discharging requirements and are generally more expensive than their vented cell equivalents. Since the electrolyte cannot be topped up, it is important to avoid regular gassing. Sealed batteries are usually not totally sealed; they incorporate some vent valves, which can release gases and vapour if the battery is over-charged. They are often described as 'valve regulated lead-acid' (VRLA) batteries.

Battery alloys

The lead used in many batteries is alloyed with other elements to achieve desirable properties, such as:

Antimony – improves strength and cycling ability; increases water consumption

Calcium – reduces water consumption (for low maintenance) at cost of reduced cycle life

Selenium – improves strength and cycling (replacement for antimony)

Safety First

Batteries are hazardous devices, containing large quantities of concentrated energy, and corrosive, explosive and poisonous materials. An awareness of these hazards, and how to minimise them, is essential for anyone with a renewable energy system

Summary of battery types

Battery type	Typical cost (100Ah)	Cycle life (50% discharge)	Main power uses	Pros system use	Cons
SLI vehicle	£40	150	Starting lights and ignition	Generator starting; occasional lighting /music supply	Cheap; widely available	Very poor cycle life
Leisure	£50-70	300	Caravans, motorhomes boats	Small solar or vehicle system	Fairly cheap; available	Short cycle life
Deep cycle vented	£100-130	1300	Static RE systems; standby power; traction	Good for domestic systems	Long cycle life; durable	Expensive; maintenance required
Deep cycle VRLA	£160+	1500	Standby; small traction – wheel chairs, golf carts; RE systems	Specialised systems – medical, telecom;	Long cycle life; no acid spills; no maintenance	Expensive; precise charge control required

incorporating battery storage.

Batteries emit combinations of hydrogen and oxygen (called 'gassing'), particularly when on charge or after charging. These are explosive!

- Do not use matches or other naked lights nearby.
- Do not smoke near a battery.
- Do not allow any electrical sparks near a battery.
- Always switch a battery charger off before connecting or disconnecting it.
- Take care not to short out the battery with tools, necklaces, etc.
- Only charge batteries in a well ventilated area.
- Batteries also contain sulphuric acid, which is very corrosive and will cause burns if it comes in contact with skin.
- Always wear protective clothing (e.g. rubber gloves, rubber apron) and goggles when working with batteries.
- Always keep a sterilised eye bath in the battery room.
- If contact with the skin does occur, immediately wash the area with lots of clean water, and if burning has occurred seek medical advice.
- If acid gets comes into contact with sensitive areas such as the eyes, medical advice should be sought immediately after washing.
- In the event of spillage on non-living matter, the acid can be neutralised with a mild alkali such as sodium carbonate (bicarbonate of soda), then washed with lots of water. Specially designed battery spill kits are also available to neutralise any spillage.

Even a fairly flat battery can deliver a large charge into a short circuit, easily enough to melt a cable and start a fire. Batteries should never be left where tools or other pieces of metal may fall across the terminals.

- Any cable connected to a battery should be protected by a correctly rated fuse.
- If possible, cover exposed terminals or the entire battery to prevent accidental shorts.
- Keep batteries out of the reach of children.

For further information on battery safety see BS 6287 (1982), 'Codes of practice for the safe operation of traction cells'.

Connecting banks of batteries

For all but the smallest off-grid systems, it will be necessary to use more than one battery to obtain the storage capacity required and/or the chosen system voltage.

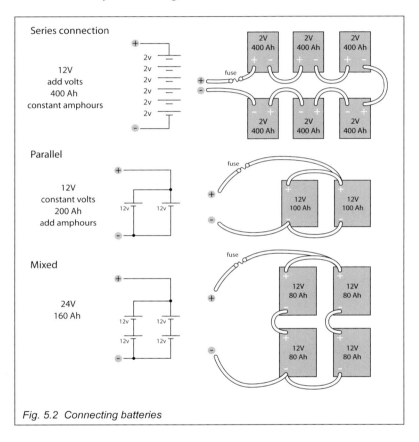

Fig. 5.2 Connecting batteries

Series connection

If the voltage of the batteries you have available is less than that of the system, you will need to connect batteries in series to increase the bank's voltage. This involves connecting batteries positive to negative, adding their voltages until you reach the required level. This approach increases voltage whilst keeping amp-hour rating constant (see Fig. 5.2).

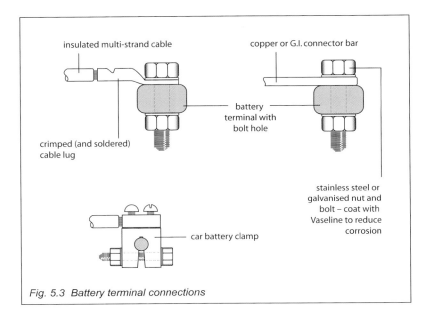

Fig. 5.3 Battery terminal connections

Parallel connection

If you need more capacity (amp-hours) at the same voltage as the batteries, you will need to connect the batteries in parallel, positive-to-positive, negative-to-negative. This way, the voltage remains constant but the amp-hour rating is added. It is important that the batteries are identical as connection of dissimilar batteries can result in some receiving less charge than others with a consequent loss of efficiency and battery life. It is best to connect the main leads diagonally across the battery bank in order to balance current flow (see Fig. 5.2).

Physical connections

Use the thickest multi-strand cable (welding cable is ideal) you can find to connect batteries together. Bolted connections through soldered, crimped lugs are excellent if the battery terminals have bolt holes. Solid copper bars are even better. Otherwise, use clamp connectors, available from automotive spares suppliers. Do not use crocodile clips except for the most temporary of installations (see Fig. 5.3).

Battery cables must be rated well in excess of the maximum expected load or charge current – be sure to consider surge loads on inverters.

Measuring state of charge

Using a hydrometer

How do you know how much charge a battery is holding? State of charge can be measured with a digital voltmeter, but the reading is affected if current (energy) is flowing into or out of the battery. The cheapest reliable way to estimate the state of charge of a battery is to use a hydrometer. This will give the relative density (or specific gravity – s.g.) of the electrolyte compared to that of water, which can be used to give an indication of state of charge either from general bands on the hydrometer itself or by looking up the reading in a table. This must be compensated for temperature if an accurate reading is required. This method is not possible with sealed batteries.

The sulphuric acid in the battery electrolyte is more dense than water – with an s.g. of 1.840. As a battery is charged, the concentration of acid increases, and so does its s.g. As the battery is discharged, the electrolyte becomes more dilute so the s.g. decreases. Specific gravity can therefore be used to find the 'state of charge' of a battery – how much energy it contains.

• A fully charged battery has an s.g. of 1.260 to 1.280
• A flat battery has an s.g of about 1.100

Typical hydrometers consist of a glass tube with a rubber bulb at the top, a rubber nozzle at the bottom and a weighted float marked with a scale in the middle. There are also plastic versions containing hinged floats that are easy to read and more robust. A third type uses coloured balls that float at different s.g. but these are not precise enough for this use.

Battery voltage

Measuring the terminal voltage is another method of estimating state of charge. The method's advantages are that it is quick and the cells of the battery do not need to be opened, thus avoiding the risk of contamination. However, terminal voltage is also a

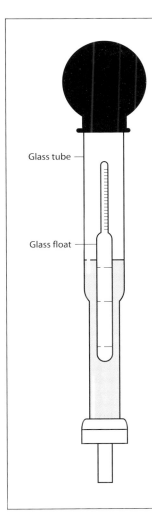

Glass tube

Glass float

Hydrometer procedure
To measure the specific gravity of a cell (one section of a battery with a voltage of roughly 2 volts) use the following procedure.
• Put on safety goggles, rubber gloves and apron to protect your eyes, hands and clothes.
• Remove the vent cap on the cell.
• Check that the electrolyte is covering the battery plates – if not you must add distilled water (NOT tap or rain water) after you have taken the s.g. reading.
• Squeeze the rubber bulb.
• Place the nozzle into the electrolyte.
• Release the bulb – the hydrometer tube will fill with electrolyte. If the float does not lift off the bottom of the tube, squeeze the bulb again.
• Gently tap the tube if bubbles are stuck to the float.
• Read the scale with your eye level with the bottom of the liquid surface.
• Put the nozzle back into the cell and gently squeeze the bulb to return the electrolyte.
• Make sure all the electrolyte drains out and be careful of drips falling onto your feet or clothes.
• Record the cell number and the s.g. reading.
• Replace the vent cap.

function of several other variables, including charge or discharge rate, temperature and, to some extent, the type of cell construction and age. Consult your battery supplier for further information. Disconnect the battery from the rest of the system by removing the main fuse to remove the effect of current flow on the voltage and allow it to stabilise for 10 minutes or so. When disconnecting batteries, be sure to also disconnect power sources first since many charge controllers can be damaged if current is flowing in from PVs or wind turbines but has nowhere to go. As with specific gravity, the relation of voltage to state of charge varies with temperature.

Battery monitors

Several manufacturers produce 'state of charge' battery meters that use microprocessors to monitor performance. Generally costing £100 or more, some monitors will even interface with a personal computer. These are the easiest way to keep close track of your system's 'fuel tank', but it is still wise to check individual cells occasionally.

Battery care
Charging protection

For good lead-acid battery life, it is essential to avoid over-charging. In all systems using lead-acid batteries it is important to limit the on-charge voltage. This will protect them against over-charging, which causes excessive 'gassing' and overheating, resulting in permanent plate damage and loss of electrolyte. Charge regulation is described later in Chapter 7 which covers control equipment. This is particularly important with sealed or 'gel' lead-acid cells which need accurate regulation of the on-charge voltage to the value recommended by the manufacturer since electrolyte lost as gas cannot be replenished.

Temperature compensation

Battery characteristics vary with temperature, storing more energy (but reducing life) as temperature increases. If the battery temperature is likely to regularly vary by more than about 8ºC, battery performance and life will benefit from a controller with a temperature compensation facility that adjusts the on-charge voltage limit as the temperature varies. Battery stores should provide protection from extreme temperatures.

Discharge protection

The other essential for good lead-acid life is to avoid frequent deep-discharges (i.e. running the battery flat or nearly so). A battery will tolerate this occasionally provided that it is recharged immediately. If it is left in a discharged state, it will quickly become permanently damaged resulting in a serious loss of storage capacity. Unfortunately, this is exactly what is likely to happen in an RE system, because once you have discharged the battery, you can't turn on the sun or wind to rescue the situation! The only safe approach is never to discharge the battery fully. Fitting an automatic 'load-disconnect' relay will help avoid disasters. Many PV controllers and inverters include these as standard.

Battery maintenance

Regularly check the state of charge. The best tool to use with vented cells is a hydrometer (see page 71), which measures the specific gravity of the electrolyte in each cell. This will show if any cells have deteriorated. Alternatively, use an accurate voltmeter after disconnecting the battery and the power sources from the rest of the system (see above). If you have several batteries connected together, disconnect the positive terminals to measure each battery voltage separately. This will show up any batteries that are beginning to fail. Keeping records on each battery over time will help you to detect failing cells.

The electrolyte should be checked regularly and topped up as required with pure distilled or de-ionised water from a non-metallic container. Never top up a battery with acid!

Batteries should be kept clean and dry, as dirt and moisture can provide a path for electricity and cause discharge, and any impurities that find their way into the electrolyte will cause problems.

Battery terminals should be periodically cleaned and coated with petroleum jelly (Vaseline®) to prevent corrosion.

Check that all the vent plugs are in place, and that battery covers are sound.

Do not leave them in a discharged condition, particularly at low temperatures as a discharged battery may freeze suffering permanent damage.

Equalisation

With vented cells, it is a good idea to occasionally give them an 'equalising charge'. This involves charging them to a voltage 0.5 to 1 volt above normal. This causes gassing, which mixes the electrolyte and can dislodge sulphate deposits on the plates. Sophisticated solar charge controllers sometimes do this automatically once a month or after a low-voltage disconnection. See Chapter 7, Control and Monitoring, for more information. Do not try to equalise sealed (VRLA) batteries.

For better battery life	
DO	**DON'T**
Protect from temperature extremes	Flatten
Store in secure, ventilated area	Leave discharged
Keep first aid and safety kit on hand	Charge or discharge too quickly
Use charge and load controllers	Forget to use fuses
Keep clean	Mix old and new, or different types
Regularly check electrolyte and state of charge	
Equalise charge (not sealed types)	

Replacing batteries

Eventually, batteries will reach the end of their cycle life. If you have several batteries connected in parallel, one may start to fail before the others. If, as advised, they are of the same type and age, it is best to replace the whole bank in one go. Mixing old and new batteries will prevent the new ones from reaching full charge.

How long will a battery last?

If looked after properly, the main factor affecting a battery's life is depth of discharge, i.e. how far it is discharged, and how often. A period of charging and recharging is called a 'cycle'; the deeper the cycle, the shorter the battery life. If the depth of discharge can be limited, the battery will last longer. Running a battery until it is totally flat will quickly destroy it! Discharge depths of between 50% and 80% are the optimum for deep cycle batteries. Some manufacturers give an indication of how many cycles to a specified depth their batteries are expected to provide. In general, a good deep-cycle battery should give at least 1000 cycles to 50%.

Do not discharge a battery too quickly. Batteries are not 100% efficient. Their efficiency varies according to how they are treated. At higher rates of discharge (C/1 to C/5) the efficiency of the battery falls to around 60%. At lower rates of discharge (C/10 to C/100) efficiency rises to around 90%. The available capacity of the battery also varies with the discharge rate. As a rule of thumb, the rate of discharge should be no greater than C/10.

Older batteries are less efficient. As a battery is cycled, it loses available capacity, and more charging energy is lost in the cell. The battery will also be more prone to self-discharge if left without charging.

Battery life is completely dependent on how the batteries are treated, and how frequently they are cycled. However, if they are well looked after and protected from over-discharge, a new deep-cycle battery can be expected to last between five and ten years, while a 'leisure' battery should last one to three years. Batteries also have a 'shelf life' so that after twelve to fifteen years, even with minimal cycling, a battery will have lost much of its original capacity.

Buying new batteries

If you are buying your own batteries, as always, it makes sense to shop around. The web and Yellow Pages are good places to start. Auto-battery shops sometimes carry leisure batteries. Caravan and boating suppliers should have a wider range and many manufacturers are accessible online. Renewable energy suppliers usually stock deep-cycle types of battery and should be able to give you advice on what will perform best. Make a list of your requirements:
- Amp-hour capacity, system voltage.
- Estimated daily and maximum discharge.
- Size or weight restrictions.
- Mobile or low-maintenance conditions.
- Available budget.

To compare batteries, you need a specification sheet. This should contain physical properties and description, capacity at different discharge currents, a graph of voltage (and specific gravity) against state of charge with adjustment rate for temperature. The crucial information is the expected cycle life for different depths of discharge. How many times will it get you through calm cloudy days before it loses its strength? Unfortunately, many manufacturers are reluctant to commit themselves to expected lifetimes because of the impact and influence of operating conditions. At the least, the supplier should give you a convincing estimate of how long it will last at your estimated loading.

Buying second-hand batteries

Batteries are expensive, but you can obtain reasonably priced second-hand ones. As with any second-hand purchase it is important to check their condition and whether they have been well looked after.

Where to look

Possible sources of second-hand deep-cycle batteries include:
- back-up power supplies for large computer systems, emergency lighting and telephone exchanges,
- submarine batteries (usually very large),
- traction batteries from milk floats, fork-lifts, golf carts and wheelchairs,
- military electronics surplus, especially communications systems.

Due to their environmentally hazardous nature, dealers in scrap and second-hand batteries are supposed to be registered – check with your local authority, they should know of anyone in your area. There is also a chance that you may be able to get batteries direct from their previous users – try manufacturers and users of the equipment listed above.

What to look for

The simplest indicator of a battery's remaining life is knowledge of its previous use. Why has it been scrapped?

Old traction cells, especially from industrial applications will have been deeply cycled and consequently have little life remaining. In contrast, batteries from float charging applications such as back-up power supplies will have spent most of their working life fully charged with only occasional deep cycles.

Visual inspection This can indicate how the battery has been physically treated. Check that the casing and terminals are in good condition; no cells are dry; if the casing is transparent – that there are no damaged plates and minimal sediment at the bottom.

State of charge This can be simply measured using a voltmeter or, better still, a hydrometer.

Fully charged? (12.5-13.5V, or 2.0-2.3V for single cells) – a battery stored flat will be impaired.

Voltages below 10V (for a 12V battery) probably indicate a dead cell.

Discharge testing Testing a battery under load gives a better idea of its ability to store charge. There are two ways to do this. Both require the battery to be fully charged before the test.

The fast method is to use a heavy discharge tester such as those used by auto battery suppliers and garages. These use two prongs or cable clips to connect a high current load and voltmeter. The prongs are placed firmly across the battery terminals and a current of 50 to 100 amps flows for ten seconds whilst the meter is observed for deflection. A healthy battery of 80 amp-hour capacity or more should not drop below 12V during the test, and afterwards the voltage should return to what it was before the test. Do not try this test on small batteries as you will probably damage them. A smaller, 10 to15 amp version can be made by connecting two car headlamps in parallel with a digital voltmeter and the battery.

A slower but more accurate method is the deep discharge test. This involves flattening the battery over ten hours using a known resistive load and comparing the final voltage to that given in the battery specification. In reality, second-hand batteries rarely come with spec sheets so you will have to estimate the expected results. As an example, a typical vented battery will be about 80% discharged when it reaches 11V at 20ºC. If its rated capacity is 100 amp-hours a load of 8 amps over 10 hours (i.e. 80 amp-hours) should leave it at this voltage. The load can be calculated using Ohm's Law (V = I R) to be 1.5 Ω. If the final voltage is significantly less, then it indicates that the battery's charge capacity has been seriously impaired. Remember to recharge the battery as soon as you finish!

Chapter 6
Converting DC to AC with Inverters

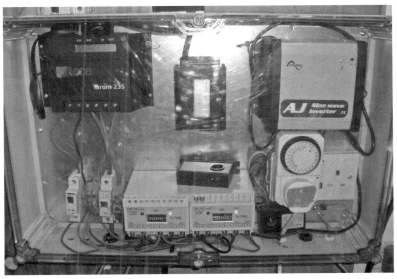

A charge controller inverter and logging equipment.

What are inverters?

We have looked at running loads on direct current – 12 volt lights and stereos are widely available, but where can you find a 12 volt video recorder or food mixer? Although these devices may exist it is much simpler to go the way of the grid-connected world. In Europe, domestic appliances run on 230 volts AC, alternating at 50 hertz (Hz, cycles per second). An inverter is a device to convert low-voltage DC power from batteries to mains voltage AC. Domestic inverters range from a hand-sized box of electronics, which can be fairly simple and cheap, to a large steel cabinet weighing around 50kg. The two main things that determine the size, complexity and cost of an inverter are:

• power – output required to meet peak load (typically 100W to 5kW in domestic use)
• waveform – how the inverter output mimics the electricity produced by conventional generators.

The best waveform, which is indistinguishable from mains power, is a sine wave. A sine wave inverter will power any sort of appliance without problems, provided that is has an adequate power rating. In the past, sine wave inverters were very expensive so simpler, cheaper devices producing square waves and modified square waves (often erroneously marketed as 'modified sine wave') found a ready market. Many appliances, especially inductive loads such as fluorescent lights and motors, do not operate very well, if at all, on a square wave. Modified square waves overcome some but not all of these load restrictions – many appliances operate less efficiently on these waveforms. With recent developments in the use of microprocessor-based electronics sine wave inverters are much more affordable, though modified square wave units can provide an economical choice, especially for bulk power. Square wave inverters are not worth the trouble these days.

Typical costs range from £0.50 to £1 per watt, and will depend on the waveform, efficiency and any other facilities which are included, such as, for example, automatic load-sensing switch on/off to minimise unnecessary battery drain.

Most inverters aimed at the domestic market are standalone, or 'self-commutating', which means that they operate without any external signal. With the increasing interest in small grid-connected systems, some larger sine wave inverters include a grid-link capability. These inverters synchronise their output waveform with an external source such as a generator or the grid, and sometimes described as 'line-commutated'. In fact, most of them can also operate in a self-commutated mode as well.

This section concentrates on the standalone static (i.e. where the power conversion is achieved electronically, with no moving parts) type of inverter. These are now quite common in the form of uninterruptible power supplies for computers, and as AC power sources in vehicles. Their use in small standalone RE systems does pose some particular problems, however. Principally, these are to do with the energy losses, which can be as much as the load supplied, and the often unknown and wide-ranging loads which the inverter is expected to power.

Different load appliances have different levels of tolerance to inverter characteristics, such as output waveform (sine, square and modified), frequency stability and the precision of output voltage regulation. Similarly, inverters have different levels of tolerance to load characteristics such as short-term current surges or reactive currents.

Specifying an inverter that can cope with any type of load is be very expensive, so a careful assessment of the requirements is justified.

Principles of operation

The DC input is connected by solid-state semiconductor switches to the primary coil of a transformer. The transformer ratio is chosen to achieve the required output voltage. By controlling the semi-conductor switches, the polarity of the transformer primary voltage can be periodically reversed, or reduced to zero.

Waveforms

In basic single-phase inverters, two or four switches are used in the 'half-bridge' or 'full-bridge' configuration (Fig.6.1). Simply reversing the primary voltage every 10 milliseconds results in a 50Hz square wave output.

Since the switches are either fully on or fully off, the power dissipated in them is small. However, this on-or-off constraint,

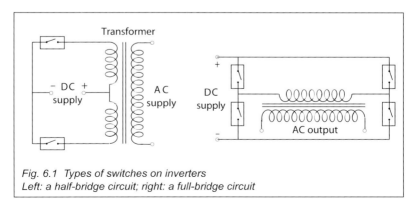

Fig. 6.1 Types of switches on inverters
Left: a half-bridge circuit; right: a full-bridge circuit

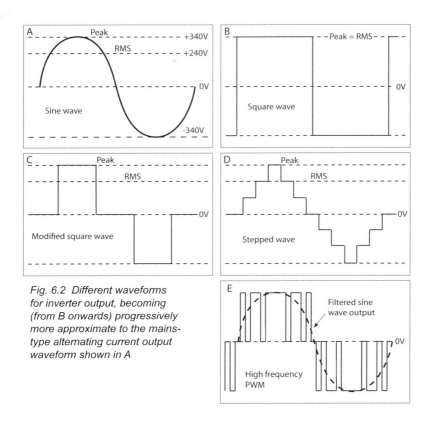

Fig. 6.2 Different waveforms for inverter output, becoming (from B onwards) progressively more approximate to the mains-type alternating current output waveform shown in A

although necessary for high efficiency, makes it difficult to generate sine waves so various approximations are used. The resulting waveform is often then filtered to make it more sinusoidal. Fig. 6.2 compares the normal mains waveform with the approximations commonly used.

Peak and Root Mean Square (r.m.s.) Voltages

A 240 volt r.m.s. sine wave has a peak of 340 volts, a ratio of 1.41 to the r.m.s. A square wave, for which the ratio is 1, cannot be simultaneously correct for both r.m.s.-sensitive and peak-sensitive loads. If a square wave inverter is to supply just incandescent lamps, for example, we could choose a transformer ratio to give +/- 240 volts; for an all peak-sensitive load +/- 340 volts would be nearer the ideal. In practice a compromise is sometimes possible as many devices are quite voltage-tolerant, and the broader peak of the square wave to some extent compensates for a reduced peak voltage. The modified square wave of Fig. 6.2 allows both the r.m.s. and peak voltages to be brought within more acceptable limits simultaneously, although it should be remembered that voltage regulation by varying the pulse width will only control the r.m.s. and not the peak level. These problems are removed by using an inverter with a more sinusoidal waveform.

It is worth noting that meters intended for use on normal sinusoidal supplies may give misleading readings on other waveforms. Moving-iron meters and 'true r.m.s.' meters will read the r.m.s. values of most waveforms adequately, but most budget digital multimeters actually measure mean rectified voltage and will not be accurate on non-sinusoidal waveforms.

The 'modified square wave'

This is an improvement over the basic square wave as it contains less unwanted harmonics and is therefore easier to clean up by low-pass filtering (Fig. 6.2). It also introduces the possibility of output voltage regulation to compensate for variations in battery voltage and load-dependent losses. This is achieved by varying the duration of the zero voltage portion of the waveform. This technique provides satisfactory voltage control when an output filter is used, but cannot control the peak voltage of the output when used without a filter.

A closer approximation to a sine wave can be achieved by the stepped wave of Fig. 6.2. This is generated by using an increased number of switches to rapidly change the transformer ratio or by adding together several two-level waveforms. The filter can be much smaller and again voltage control can be achieved by varying the proportions of time spent at the different levels.

Pulse width modulation (PWM)

PWM inverters have become popular over the last few years. This technique involves switching the primary voltage rapidly between two or three levels and varying the time spent at each, such that the average of the voltage is sinusoidal (Fig. 6.2). A very simple and compact filter can then easily remove the switching frequency, provided that it is much higher than the output frequency required. A further recent development uses a very high frequency inverter and rectifier to produce a high DC voltage (typically 340 volts). This is then switched, as in the previous types, to produce an appropriate output waveform. The main advantage is that the high frequency transformer is tiny and the whole inverter can be smaller and lighter.

Several different types of power semiconductor are used in inverters. The power semiconductors are usually driven by an accurate oscillator which ensures a constant output frequency and feeds timing circuits which achieve voltage control, perhaps output current limiting, and avoid switching overlap (one switch coming on before the previous one has fully turned off, which could cause very high current peaks). In some simple inverters, the switches are driven via a saturating drive transformer, fed from the inverter's own output transformer. These are referred to as 'self-oscillating' inverters, and they usually lack accurate control of frequency and output voltage.

Efficiency

The efficiency is generally taken to be (power out) ÷ (power in) expressed as a percentage. The efficiency of a particular inverter is not a constant; it varies continually with changing operating conditions. The load power, load power-factor and input voltage all affect it.

Fig. 6.3 shows how efficiency varies with load power for several different inverters. All have a poor efficiency at low loads and the best performing of these at low loads are not necessarily the best at high loads. The low-load efficiency is often particularly important for small standalone wind and solar power systems, as inverter power rating is often chosen to suit a high power appliance which is used for only a short time each day; most of the time the inverter is operating at a small fraction of rated output with very poor efficiency. The effect on estimated energy consumption can be catastrophic. Such problems can be minimised by the use of 'start-on-demand' circuits which only turn the inverter on when a load is applied. Inverter losses are of several distinct types (see Fig.6.4).

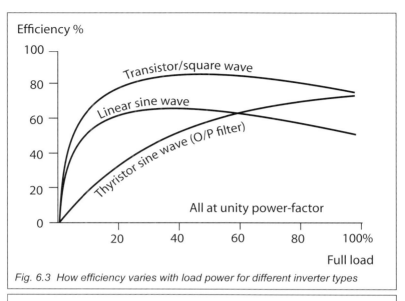

Fig. 6.3 How efficiency varies with load power for different inverter types

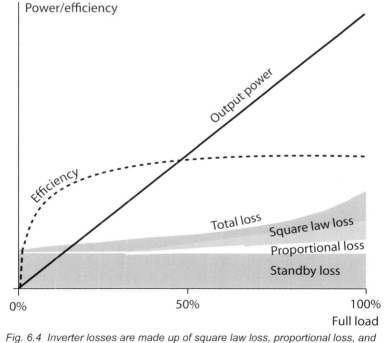

Fig. 6.4 Inverter losses are made up of square law loss, proportional loss, and standby loss. Here they are seen in relation to efficiency and output power

Standby power

Even with no load connected, the inverter consumes power in its oscillator and drive circuits, and to provide for the magnetising losses of the transformer. The transformer's magnetising current flows through the semiconductors where there is some volt-drop and inevitable power loss. In an inverter with an output filter, the transformer and semiconductor currents and hence the losses are much higher. The standby power is more or less constant, but may increase at high battery voltage. High standby losses affect the efficiency most when the inverter is predominantly used at low output power. Load search and 'sleep mode' options reduce standby losses by switching off the inverter until a load is detected.

Proportional losses

These are due to voltage drops across semiconductor junction devices, i.e. diodes, bipolar transistors and thyristors. The resulting power loss is roughly proportional to output power, and affects the efficiency equally over the whole output power range.

Square law losses

These are mainly due to resistance in the system; transformer windings, semiconductor resistance, and battery cables are the main contributors. Semiconductor switching losses also tend to be proportional to the square of the output power, although this does depend on the drive circuit design; they are also proportional to the switching frequency. The effect of all these losses on efficiency is worst at maximum power output.

Power-factor losses

Reactive loads – those that include capacitors or coils such as fluorescent lights and motors – increase proportional and square losses, resulting in reduced efficiency whenever the power-factor is less than unity. Reactive power flows whenever the output current is not in phase with the voltage, and consists of pulses of energy oscillating back and forth between the source and the load; it increases losses, but transfers no useful power. The power factor is defined as the cosine of the phase angle between the current and voltage waves. The useful, or 'real', power is given by:

Real Power = Power Factor x Voltage x Current

Breaking the inverter losses down into the above types allows accurate modelling of their effect on total system efficiency, even with widely varying loads. Figure 6.4 shows how the various losses contribute to the overall efficiency curve. Reputable manufacturers should provide such a curve in their product specification sheet. Since efficiency is a key selling point, many manufacturers have applied much ingenuity to reduce losses. Many modern inverters are over 90% efficient for most of their operating range, and consume only a few watts at standby.

Mixed loads

Most systems have a combination of light and heavy loads running for different periods. The inverter must be sized for the largest expected load such as a pump, workshop equipment or washing machine. Most of the time, the inverter may only be called on to supply small loads such as fluorescent lights, fax machine, answer-phone or a radio, typically under 15 watts. Even a high specification inverter rated at 2 to 3kW will waste 10 to 20 watts running such loads, and if they are running continuously this can add up to a lot of wasted watt-hours. One solution is to run such small loads on 12 volt DC but this has disadvantages as we have already seen. Another approach is to run separate AC circuits for high and low power applications, and use two inverters – a big one for bulk power, and a small sine wave unit to provide affordable high quality and efficient supply for fluorescent lighting and electronic equipment.

Phantom loads

Many modern electronic appliances include another potential cause of losses – 'phantom' loads. These are small continuous loads that bring little benefit but can play havoc with load search circuits and inverter efficiency. Classic examples are TV standby circuits, phone and shaver chargers and video recorder clocks. A simple solution is to switch all appliances/gadgets off at the socket when not in use.

Input and output characteristics
Output current

The inverter output capability is usually quoted as a 'VA' rating, which is the product of r.m.s. output voltage and maximum r.m.s. output current. There may be a restricted range of power-factor for which this maximum current is available. The inverter's output power will only reach the VA rating with a resistive load, i.e. power-factor = 1. The output current must be limited by the inverter in some way to avoid damage to the semiconductors in the case of overloads. Unlike the mains supply, the maximum current available before permanent damage occurs is often only slightly above the normal operating current. This means that many inverters are not capable of blowing fuses or even tripping circuit breakers that are rated near to their maximum output current. To avoid damage under any possible overload condition, the inverter may often have a very fast-acting electronic trip to catch high transient current faults and a slow trip to protect against prolonged, relatively small overloads which would cause overheating.

Motor starting usually requires a high current often at a very low power factor; unless the inverter rating is matched to this, a trip will operate, or the inverter will be damaged. Inverters with non-sinusoidal outputs are likely to trip or be damaged by the use of power-factor correction capacitors, as these cause high transient currents at each step change in instantaneous output voltage.

Better inverters are often designed to provide currents two to five times their rated output for short periods (5 seconds to 5 minutes) in order to cope with motor start-up current surges.

Output voltage

This may or may not be regulated, and as explained earlier, with the simpler designs, the r.m.s. or the mean rectified voltage may be controlled whilst the peak is not. Even with output voltage regulation, there is often some residual voltage variation depending on load current and on battery voltage – considerably more variation than we expect from the mains. There are two common problems with the dynamics of the voltage control loop. One is the considerable voltage overshoot that commonly occurs when the load is suddenly reduced; this can cause damage to some appliances. The other is the voltage instability that can occur when the load current fluctuates at the natural frequency of the voltage control feedback loop. This can easily occur with motors with periodic load torque fluctuations.

Input voltage

Input voltage range is usually specified for each model by the manufacturer and the inverter could be damaged by operating it above or below this range. However, many inverters are internally protected against this misuse and against reverse polarity connection, which can otherwise have spectacular results. With widely varying supplies some voltage pre-regulation may be necessary. Battery leads should be sized for low voltage drop at full load; even if the inverter could tolerate more volt drop, the overall system efficiency would suffer from minor economies here.

Short term input voltage variations can be a problem. Long battery leads will have a significant inductance, and any sudden current reduction due to the inverter or another load will cause a transient voltage increase that could cause inverter damage or malfunction. A ripple on the input voltage, due to an AC powered charger, for example, can cause output voltage fluctuation at the beat frequency between the ripple and the inverter's own frequency. It is possible to minimise these problems with short input leads dedicated to supplying the inverter only.

Inverter-chargers

Some inverters are available that include a battery charger, thus converting power in both directions between AC and DC. These can be used in a number of ways.

Genset plus batteries

Many people interested in using renewable energy for off-grid power supply may already have diesel or petrol generating sets (gensets), especially if they have relatively high loads such as water pumps and welders. Since the gensets will have been sized for the peak loads, much of the time they will be operating inefficiently at much lower loads. Case study 3 – Nyahode School – is a good example; the generator was intended to power workshop machine tools and welders for a few hours per day, but was also used to provide a tiny fraction of its rated output for lighting and TV in the evenings.

Using an inverter-charger, the batteries are charged during peak load periods, adding a small extra load. In the evening, rather than running the genset, the inverter takes over, providing about 500 watts of lighting and entertainment loads. Running costs for diesel and maintenance are considerably reduced, and the genset's life is greatly extended. This also makes a good intermediate step when converting from a diesel system to a hybrid system incorporating renewable sources.

Standby power systems

In many parts of the world, the mains supply can be very unreliable. Inverter-chargers can be used to keep a battery reserve on float charge during periods of supply. When a power failure occurs, the charger automatically converts to inverter mode, providing a back-up supply. Depending on the load and capacity of the batteries, this can operate for anything from an hour or so to several days. Even in the UK, where the mains supply is considered to be very reliable, similar systems are used to guarantee power for telephone exchanges and computer systems.

Load requirements
Effects of different waveforms

Many loads will operate satisfactorily on non-sinusoidal waveforms. The main problems arise from incorrect voltage levels and from overheating due to the high harmonic content of the waveform. Heating elements and incandescent lamps are sensitive only to the 'r.m.s.' (root mean square) voltage of the applied waveform; provided that this is correct, there will be no problem except perhaps a slight audible buzz from the appliance. Appliances that convert the AC supply back to DC by rectifying and smoothing (such as most electronic equipment: radios, TVs, etc., and 'high-frequency' fluorescent lighting fittings) are sensitive to the peak voltage of the waveform.

Operating motors on non-sinusoidal waveforms should be approached with caution. There is generally little problem with 'Universal' motors, as found in electric drills, most small food mixers, etc. Motors that are operated for longer periods, particularly induction motors, may suffer from overheating due to increased

Examples of inverter specifications

Inverter A
AC output: 230 volts, 1200W
continuous for P.F 0.6 to 1, 1800W
for 15 min, 4000W
for 5 sec
Output voltage stability: +/-3%
Frequency: 50Hz. +/-0.01%
Waveform: Pure sine wave
Harmonic distortion:
<2% at full power
Input voltage: 24 volts nom.
Range: 21 to 32 volts
Ambient temperature: rated at
25°C, forced cooling at 45°C
Standby power consumption:
5W, 0.5W in sleep mode
Efficiency: full load: 89%,
1/2 load: 92%, 1/4 load: 90%
Weight: 13kg

Inverter B
AC output: 240 volts,1800 watts
continuous, 2100 watts for 1 hour
Output voltage stability: +/-2%
Frequency: 50Hz. +/-0.02%
Waveform: modified square wave
('Quasi-sine' – manufacturer)
Input voltage: 24 volts nom.
Range: 18 to 31 volts
Ambient temp: ratings at 20°C,
internal power limit reduces at
higher temperatures
Standby power consumption:
4 watts, 0.3 watts in sleep mode
Efficiency: 1800W, 90%; 900W,
94%; 300W, 95%; 50W, 90%
Overload: 3000W, within operating
voltage spec.,
at 24V input; 5000W
absolute max.
Weight: 16kg

than sine wave types. Square wave units may be cheaper still, but these days are rarely worth the reduced functionality.

Desirable features
In addition to finding a device with a suitable power output, waveform and high efficiency, there are other features that are worth looking for in a prospective inverter.

Load sensing / sleep mode
As mentioned above, some inverters have the ability to switch themselves off when not in use, considerably reducing standby consumption to less than a watt by emitting a load-seeking pulse that reawakens the inverter when a load is connected. This can cause problems with phantom loads such as VCR clocks and TV standby circuits, so the ability to adjust the trigger threshold is useful.

Surge ability
Since many motor loads require high starting currents, the ability to produce two or three times its rated output for a few seconds

saves having to size the inverter for momentary high loads.

Output regulation

Both peak and r.m.s. voltages should be regulated to within 10% of their nominal values to prevent damage to sensitive loads. Some small, budget inverters are not regulated and consequently output varies with battery voltage and the nature of the load.

Output frequency should also be strictly regulated and sine wave harmonic distortion should be under 1%.

Interference suppression

The high speed switching circuits of many inverters often produce radio frequency interference (RFI) that should be adequately suppressed to prevent its interference with sensitive equipment such as video/dvd players and music systems.

Adequate protection

Inverters should be internally protected from:
• High battery voltages
• Reverse polarity connection to the battery
• High load currents
• Over-heating

Low voltage disconnection

Better inverters protect themselves from low battery voltages, also preventing over-discharge of the battery bank.

Battery charging

If you have access to other AC power sources such as the mains or a genset this makes a compact hybrid system. Check for a multi-stage charging regime; temperature compensation will help the batteries in variable climates. If you have doubts about the regulation of the external AC source, it may be safer to go for a separate charger to safeguard the inverter.

Remote control

Some larger inverters can be operated and monitored via a remote control panel, which is handy if the inverter is installed away from the main living area.

Solar charge regulation

Some inverters now include a built in solar regulator, which makes installation a lot neater and can save money. Check that the specifications and charging regime match the specification of a comparable separate unit.

Parallel connection

If a system has been designed using multiple inverters, or it is anticipated that additional ones will be added at a later date, it is very helpful if they can operate in parallel with synchronised output and an ability to shut down unneeded units.

Inverter care

Always keep inverters in a cool, well ventilated, and dry place. Do not mount an inverter above a vented battery because there is a potential for sparks during switching and gas given off during charging can corrode the circuitry.

Conclusion

When choosing an inverter, there will inevitably be a compromise between versatility, efficiency and economy. The inverter should be capable of supplying the maximum expected load, but if it will generally run at far lower loads consider one with good low-load efficiency, or use two, one for general use and the other to meet peak demand. Square wave units can provide a cheap rough and ready supply for limited applications but for daily general use you're better off paying a bit more for modified square wave or sine wave output. Although the former may often appear more efficient, many loads operate less efficiently on the modified wave form so the overall losses can be greater than with a sine wave unit. Good modified square wave devices are a cheaper option for less sensitive and occasional heavy loads. Pure sine wave is the ideal, and increasingly competitive in price.

Key points to consider are:
• waveform;
• output level and regulation;

- protection;
- efficiency;
- cost;
- proven reliability.

Chapter 7
Controlling and Monitoring Your Power

Why control your system?

Control equipment protects you and your system from danger or damage caused by faults in the supply or loads. In a mains-connected system, internal wiring is protected at the distribution board from load faults such as short circuits and earth leakage by fuses, miniature circuit breakers (MCBs) and residual current or earth-leakage circuit breakers (RCCBs and ELCBs). The supply is regulated at the power station by the power generating company and through the transmission system by the regional electricity company. In off-grid systems, the entire system must be controlled and regulated by the user. Controls are necessary for several reasons:

- to optimise system performance over wide fluctuations in operating conditions;
- to deal with mismatch between collected energy and that used by the load;
- to protect system components and users;
- to provide automatic operation with minimum human involvement.

The equipment used ranges from simple thermostats or voltage regulators to complete computer-based systems managing many variables in a co-ordinated manner.

Typical control functions

Control equipment may be called upon to perform the following functions:

- regulation of battery charging;
- limiting battery discharge;
- battery cell equalisation;
- reverse input current blocking;

- stabilisation of the system's load voltage;
- starting/stopping an auxiliary generator;
- diversion of surplus energy to secondary loads (dump or ballast);
- informing you of system status, perhaps with remote signalling;
- improving matching between the power source and the battery or load to optimise the power transfer;
- protection against lightning induced surges;
- protection of itself against misuse and fault conditions.

The power used by the control circuits must be small, or serious inefficiencies result. Microprocessor-based controllers often combine many of these functions with monitoring capability as well.

Battery charge limiting

To achieve optimum battery life it is necessary to protect the battery against excessive charge input and against over-discharge. The requirements are particularly severe with 'sealed' lead-acid cells, in which water lost due to overcharge can't be replenished. The battery is able to accept high charging currents when in a fairly low state of charge without significant problems, but as the state of charge increases the charging current must be reduced to limit gassing.

Charge controllers limit battery voltage to a maximum of around 2.3 volts per cell at 25°C. This causes the charging current to fall off naturally before gassing becomes a problem. A photovoltaic controller can achieve this by open circuiting or by short-circuiting the PV modules, as they behave as a constant current source. The wind turbine however is not so tolerant, so usually its controller must divert excess power to a secondary or 'dump' load once the batteries are up to their fully charged – or 'float' – voltage. Domestic water or space heating is an ideal dump load.

The battery can be left charging at the float voltage for long periods with minimal electrolyte loss. In the majority of applications, the regulator senses the battery voltage via separate battery sense leads to avoid errors caused by the voltage drop occurring due to the currents flowing in power leads. This allows it to give accurate battery voltage regulation. Cell voltage and capacity are affected by temperature (see Fig. 7.1) so better regulators allow compensation using a remote temperature sensor placed close to the batteries.

Electrically, there are two basic approaches to controlling the input power, series and shunt regulation, shown in Fig. 7.2.

Series regulation

The series method introduces a control element (a relay, electronic switch or a linear control device) into the input current path; solid state devices are preferred for long life. As the battery voltage rises to float voltage, the control element is turned off. If linear control is used the current will decrease until the input current is equal to the current required to keep the battery at float voltage and thus a stable state is reached. Fig. 7.3a.

Shunt regulation

The shunt method involves a control device, usually with a dump load connected across the power source; see Fig.7.3b. As battery

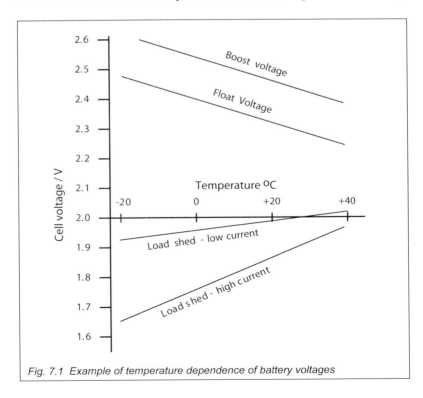

Fig. 7.1 Example of temperature dependence of battery voltages

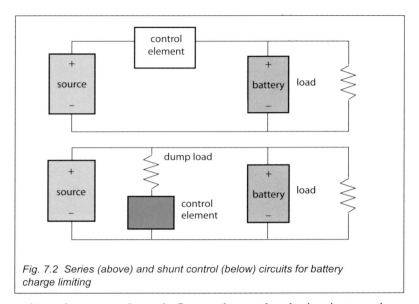

Fig. 7.2 Series (above) and shunt control (below) circuits for battery charge limiting

voltage increases through float voltage, the device is turned on (progressively or switched) to divert input current away from the battery. Relays can be used successfully by splitting the dump load into sections, each switched in by its own relay. The dump load must be rated to carry the peak input power. Dump heaters can be a bit hazardous, as they may be left completely cold for several months during which time they may be covered up carelessly or have combustible material placed next to them.

In systems where dumping is a regular occurrence, such as those based on wind and hydro turbines, it is common practice to divert the excess power to a useful load such as water heating. Immersion heaters need protecting to prevent over-heating of the water tank – a standard thermostat can operate a relay to divert the power to a secondary dump load such as an air heater.

In some situations, the dump can be dispensed with by directly short-circuiting the source with the control device. In this case, a blocking diode between the control device and the battery is essential. Some small wind generators will tolerate shorting; the method can be used with PV inputs, but advice must be sought from specific manufacturers, because short-circuited panels are more prone to damage by partial shading.

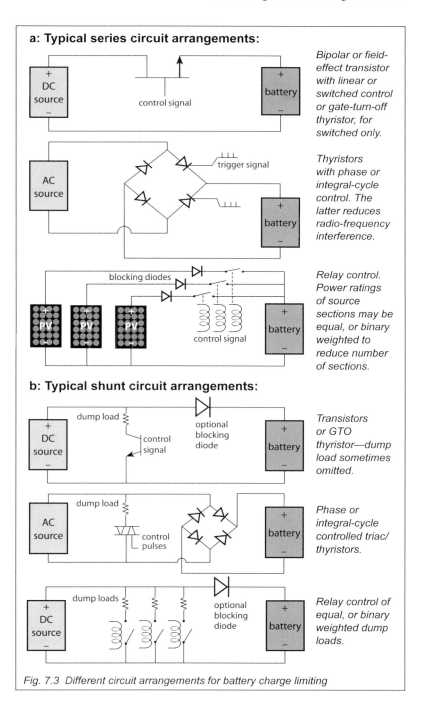

a: Typical series circuit arrangements:

DC source + − control signal battery + −

Bipolar or field-effect transistor with linear or switched control or gate-turn-off thyristor, for switched only.

AC source — trigger signal — battery + −

Thyristors with phase or integral-cycle control. The latter reduces radio-frequency interference.

blocking diodes — control signal — PV PV PV — battery + −

Relay control. Power ratings of source sections may be equal, or binary weighted to reduce number of sections.

b: Typical shunt circuit arrangements:

DC source + − dump load — control signal — optional blocking diode — battery + −

Transistors or GTO thyristor—dump load sometimes omitted.

AC source — dump load — control pulses — battery + −

Phase or integral-cycle controlled triac/ thyristors.

DC source + − dump loads — optional blocking diode — battery + −

Relay control of equal, or binary weighted dump loads.

Fig. 7.3 Different circuit arrangements for battery charge limiting

Over-discharge protection

Automatic over-discharge protection involves disconnecting the load (or all but essential high-priority loads) when a low charge state is detected. Controllers for larger applications such as PV powered hospitals or villages may allow several levels of load-shedding priority to be defined by the user. Low state of charge may be measured on a simple low-voltage basis, but the better controllers include temperature and current compensation or use a charge integration method.

Cell equalisation

Imbalance between cell capacities and leakage currents causes an increasing variation of state-of-charge between the individual cells of a battery. In static, low-power systems there is also a tendency for the electrolyte to stratify into layers of differing density. Giving a battery an occasional overcharge with vigorous gassing helps to overcome both these problems. This can be achieved simply by temporarily increasing the controller voltage setting from the float voltage to a higher 'boost voltage' (2.5-2.6V per cell at 20°C). This can be done manually or with a timer.

Matching

Designing for optimum power transfer between a wind generator or PV array and a battery involves compromises, which usually only result in a good match in some operating conditions. Wind generators optimised around their rated output condition will probably have a poor performance at cut-in speeds. Others have a good low wind performance, but sacrifice output at higher winds. With PV's, matching to a battery is inherently quite good, provided the correct number of cells is chosen and circuit voltage drops are taken into account. However, there will still be significant variation from the optimum when the full range of light level, temperature and battery voltage combinations are considered.

In many cases, matching can be improved by transforming voltage and current levels between the source and the battery by a ratio that varies as operating conditions change; such devices are often called 'maximum power point trackers'. With an AC source, a conventional transformer can be used, but with DC a switchmode converter is required. These devices are not 100% efficient, but are becoming more common on larger PV systems (1000Wp +) where their cost is offset by the extra power generated. They have also been used successfully with wind generators to reduce cut-in speeds and improve high windspeed outputs.

Other controls

Wind turbine controls for power limiting, over-speed control, yawing, pitch control, start-up, etc., are best sourced complete from the machine. Many larger solar controllers include charge regulators, low voltage load disconnects, over-current protection and some monitoring function (battery voltage, PV current) all in one box. These can be a cost effective and simple way to put a PV system together, but remember to use separate controllers for other sources such as wind generators.

Solar trackers adjust the orientation of a PV array to follow the sun through the day. Some are controlled by a shadow-plate feedback system (electronic or thermo-mechanical) or by a computer based system that calculates sun-angles for the time of day and the date. Another version uses a liquid-vapour balancing system that gradually tips the array.

DC power conditioning for specific loads

A DC supply may sometimes need improvement before it is fed to the DC loads. This is because the voltage of a battery can typically vary by -10% to +20% from its nominal value during normal operation.

Voltage regulation

For incandescent lighting (see Fig. 6.5), some DC powered electronic equipment, and for a few older inverters, this range is too wide. Improved stability can be provided with a diode-string, a linear regulator, or a switchmode regulator (Fig. 7.5).

Each diode in a diode-string causes a volt-drop of around 0.8 volts, and the diodes can be shorted electronically or manually in groups to provide crude but often adequate regulation. Suitably rated diodes with heat sinks can handle current peaks, and there need be no power loss at critical times when the battery voltage is low.

The linear regulator can provide precise voltage control but

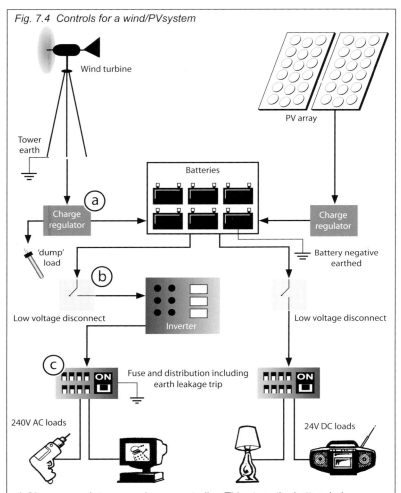

Fig. 7.4 Controls for a wind/PVsystem

a) Charge regulator ...or charge controller. This stops the battery being damaged by overcharging. It does this either by turning the power off or by diverting it to a dump load—usually a heating element.

b) Low voltage disconnect As the battery discharges, the voltage drops. When this voltage reaches a pre-set limit, the loads are automatically disconnected.

c) Fuse and distribution box, including earth leakage trip The distribution box contains fuses for the protection of the cables that distribute the power to the appliances (these should be individually fused in the plugs). The Earth Leakage Trip (also known as an RCCB, residual current circuit breaker, or ELCB, earth leakage circuit breaker) detects the difference between the current leaving and the current returning. If this becomes greater than 30mA (the maximum safe level), it switches off the power.

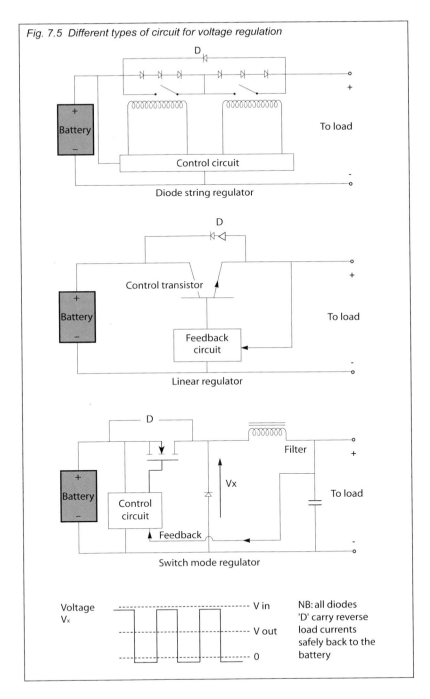

Fig. 7.5 Different types of circuit for voltage regulation

high current capability gets expensive. Like the diode-string, it must dissipate power equal to its volt-drop multiplied by the load current, and it can be shorted out by a relay to avoid losses at low battery voltage. The switchmode circuit dissipates little power, as the transistor switch is either on or off. The switching is controlled to keep the average voltage before the filter constant; the filter then removes the high frequency waveform, leaving a steady DC level. This approach is more complex but can offer better efficiency, given good design.

Different operating voltages

Certain pieces of equipment often require DC supplies at voltages other than the system voltage. For example, it may be required to operate a 12V TV on a 24V system. The best method is probably to use a switchmode circuit like the one in Fig. 6.2 in which the switching is controlled to maintain the output at 12V. Commercial units to do this are available, and have an efficiency of 70% to 90%.

Simpler units that plug into car lighter sockets use voltage regulator chips and are a cheap option for small loads but are not very efficient as excess voltage is dissipated as heat.

Protection from power surges

To protect equipment from power surges, suppressors such as 'varistors' or 'Zener-diodes' can be inserted into the circuit. These draw a high current from the supply whenever the voltage is above the threshold voltage of the equipment. Their power absorption and dissipation ratings must be enough to contain the energy in the transient power surges. The power source impedance may need to be increased to reduce the peak power. Very severe infrequent transients (due to lightning, for example) are often removed by a 'crowbar' circuit. This usually uses a thyristor connected across the supply, downstream of a fuse or current trip. If the voltage exceeds a safe value, a voltage detector circuit turns on the thyristor, which shorts the supply within a few microseconds, effectively protecting the load. If the source includes a battery, a huge current will flow and blow the fuse. An auto-reset current trip can be used in place of the fuse when the system must be restored to operation without manual intervention.

Other methods suitable for lightning protection are spark gaps, such as earthed engine sparkplugs on the output of a low voltage wind generator, and chokes – large wire coils that tend to 'flatten' voltage spikes. If you are concerned about lightning protection, consult a specialist for more advice.

Micro-hydro controllers

Very small hydros with outputs less than about 1kW, often generate DC and charge batteries; in this case the control problems are much the same as small solar and wind systems. Above this power level, a synchronous alternator is usually used to generate mains voltage AC directly.

Alternators contain two sets of windings: a main set that generates the power and a set of 'field windings' that create a magnetic field. The output voltage and frequency of these machines depend on the shaft speed (how fast the alternator is rotating) and the strength of the magnetic field.

Automatic voltage regulators

The output voltage can be stabilised at, say, 230V by an automatic voltage regulator (AVR), which is usually supplied with the alternator but this will only work over a limited speed range. The AVR senses the voltage across the main windings and adjusts the current to the field windings, thus altering the strength of the magnetic field and regulating the output voltage to the desired level.

Dump load controllers

The only way to stabilise the frequency is to maintain the correct alternator speed for the standard mains frequency (usually 1500RPM for 50Hz). In old hydro systems, this was done by controlling the water feed to the turbine, but this is difficult so modern micro-hydros use an electronic dump-load (or 'ballast-load') controller.

This type of controller works by sensing the frequency of the AC generated by the alternator, and comparing this with a pre-set standard. If the frequency starts to rise, the controller feeds some of the output power of the alternator to a 'dump' or 'ballast' load which, in practice, is usually an immersion heater or some other electric heater. The extra electrical load makes the alternator more difficult to turn, and this causes the turbine and alternator to slow down until the frequency is back to its correct value.

If a large main load is turned on, the load on the turbine will

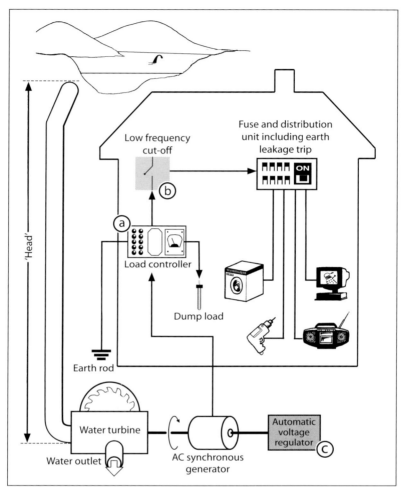

Fig. 7.6 Micro-hydro generator control system
a) **AC hydro-power load controller** An AC hydro-power system has two
loads, the main domestic load (e.g. television, lights, etc.) that has first call over
the generated power, and a ballast load (e.g. an immersion heater) that uses
any excess power.
The function of the load controller is to keep the system working correctly as
different domestic loads are turned on and off. It does this by measuring the
frequency of the AC output of the hydro generator and adjusting the amount
of power sent to the dump load, thereby maintaining the constant 50Hz output
frequency needed for the electrical appliances powered by the system to work
properly.
For example, if a large main domestic load is turned on, the turbine will
become loaded and slow down, thus reducing the frequency of the output.

will be done to the DMM, but the reading will be negative). Simple, but, like blood pressure in humans, an indicator of many subtleties you will come to appreciate as you learn about your system. Separate cell voltages will show up any weak cells, but you will need to disconnect one end if checking individual batteries connected in parallel.

AC voltages Take care! Non-r.m.s. meters will give inaccurate readings with all but pure sine waves. They calculate r.m.s. by applying a factor to the peak voltage assuming it is a sine wave. Measure between live and neutral for output voltage. Measuring to earth can show up appliance and earth faults. Useful for checking voltage levels on gensets and un-rectified wind generators. With 3 phase supplies use voltage between phases to check for balance.

Continuity and short circuits

Use the ohms (Ω) setting to check continuity of cables and fuses. Be sure to isolate the section first. Measuring between (isolated) conductors or earth can show short circuits.

Poor connections

If you find voltage drops of more than a few millivolts across a connection in a circuit, it needs securing. In incomplete circuits, use the resistance setting.

Diodes and rectifiers

Diodes are electrical 'one-way valves' they allow electricity to flow one way, but not the other. They are used to rectify alternating current (AC) into direct current (DC) that can be stored in the battery. They are also used to block current from feeding the wrong way and to drop output voltage. Set to diode setting (arrow and bar symbol), the meter applies a small voltage to the probes and the reading indicates which way the diode 'flows'. A healthy diode should show open circuit in reverse and 0.4 to 0.8 (the volt drop) forward – from positive probe to negative.

Frequency

If the DMM has a frequency setting you can check the regulation of AC supplies such as hydro and engine generators. The frequency of unrectified wind generator output will be proportional to the rotation speed, which can give you a rough idea of the windspeed (i.e. a high frequency will indicate high rotation speed in high winds).

Wind energy systems

Simple performance monitoring involves keeping some record of the windspeed and of the energy output of the system. Independent DC watt-hour or amp-hour meters can be used to measure the energy generated and the energy consumed by the load. This enables checks to be kept on battery efficiency separate from the wind generator performance. In this type of system it may also be useful to give the user an indication of the current battery state-of-charge. You can measure this manually using a hydrometer (assuming wet lead-acid batteries) or by voltage monitoring (not very accurate; some interpretation of the reading is needed) or by a more complex electronic state-of-charge meter. Care should be taken to ensure that any wires used to monitor systems are well protected by suitable resistors or fuses against high, potentially destructive, fault currents.

Solar energy systems

Performance monitoring of PV systems involves similar equipment to the wind/battery systems described above, but additional variables, such as array voltage, temperature, battery temperature and perhaps inverter performance, are also important. Where data is being collected for research purposes, it is common to monitor the solar insolation using a calibrated solar cell.

Water energy systems

This is usually kept fairly simple. Very small battery-charging systems are very similar to wind/battery systems. For the larger AC generating installations, meters are usually installed to measure voltage, frequency, 'main load' current and 'controlled load' current (heating). These allow the user to see immediately how well the system is working. The 'controlled load' current shows how much spare power is available at any moment. The 'main load' current allows a check on domestic power consumption, and on whether the system is being overloaded. Leaves partially blocking the water intake, for example, will show up as dropping frequency even when the 'main load' current is not excessive.

A further useful diagnostic aid is a water pressure gauge fitted to the feed-pipe just before the turbine (and before the shut-off valve, if fitted). This allows a check to be made on the condition of the pipe, the build-up of friction losses due, perhaps, to debris in the pipe or the presence of air bubbles. Together with flow measurement, it enables the power input to the turbine to be calculated so that, for example, unexpectedly low output power can be traced to either a water source/pipe problem, or a turbine/generator problem.

Normal AC mains-type kWh meters may be used to monitor the total energy produced over a period and how it was shared between the main domestic loads and the controlled heating load.

Battery monitors

Volt and ammeters give you a reasonable idea how energy is moving in your system, and with experience, you should be able to estimate what's left in your batteries and what it can do. However, it's a vague science – for £100 to £200 you can buy a battery monitor that will provide detailed information on system performance. These devices, such as 'E-meter' and 'TriMetric', use microprocessors to monitor charge in and out of the battery. They generally draw between 0.5 and 2 watts from the battery they are monitoring. By analysing recent cycling performance, the monitor estimates the battery capacity and operating efficiency. Multi-function displays show voltage, current, amp-hours remaining and many other performance parameters. Drops in measured efficiency indicate when equalisation is worthwhile, or the presence of failing cells. Some devices will link to a computer via an RS232 connection, enabling short-term logging. The meter should include a suitable shunt with which to measure battery current.

Data loggers

For general domestic systems, long-term performance can be monitored by regular manual recording of information from the various meters installed. With commercially installed systems, particularly for non-domestic applications, there may be a need to gather more detailed performance data in order to optimise the future design of similar systems or to inform research projects.

Some fancy metering units allow you to connect a computer and record readings. This can provide hours of fun with spreadsheets and graphs, but uses a lot of energy to keep the computer running for long periods. For those with electronics expertise, it is possible to adapt old computers to provide data logging facilities. Practical electronics publications may be able to provide circuit diagrams for basic data logging systems.

Multi-channel data loggers are far more efficient but cost hundreds to thousands of pounds. These devices record data from a variety of meters using a microprocessor to average out inputs on a periodic basis. The stored data can then be downloaded to a computer for analysis either by manual collection or remotely, using telephone modems.

Chapter 8
Connecting It All Together

This chapter examines wiring, safety measures and installation procedures. Cables use up electric power over their lengths, and this effect, called voltage drop, is also covered in this section. The exact details of installation will depend on the type of system chosen (other CAT Publications titles cover wind, PV and hydro-generators and examine the specific details relevant to each power source – see Resources).

Cabling installation

The electrical wiring associated with RE systems mostly follows standard wiring practice. Information is widely available from books and DIY manuals, so we will only discuss the important ways in which RE system wiring differs from standard practice.

If you are not sure of your competence, get a qualified electrician to do the job or to advise you, as sub-standard installations can easily cause fire or electric shock hazards. In any case, when completed, the entire system must be checked by a properly accredited electrician who will issue a Part P certificate in order to comply with legislation and Building Regulations.

Cable size and type

The cable size for conventional domestic scale installations is chosen simply on the basis of its current-carrying capacity. In other words, the cable must be thick enough to carry the required current without overheating. The tables on pages 124-125 show these absolute minimum sizes, for 12V, 24V and 240V systems.

With low voltage systems, the current (amps) for any particular type of appliance will be much higher than that used by an equivalent mains (240V AC) device. For example, a mains desk-lamp may only need 0.25 amps, whereas an equivalent 12V lamp would use 5 amps. The 12V lamp will therefore need far thicker cable than the mains lamp, in order to carry the extra current without overheating.

Cables also need to be thicker because of 'volt drop'. As current flows down a cable, some power is lost due to the resistance of the copper, 'obstructing' the flow of electrons. The lost power appears as heat warming the cable slightly along its whole length and reduces the voltage which is available at the far end. The volt-drop is worst for long cables carrying high currents, and can make some low voltage systems completely impractical because of the very thick and expensive cable needed. A volt-drop of 2V is generally unacceptable in a 12V system – with only 10V left, lights will be dim and TVs may not work. Conversely, in a normal mains system, a drop of 2V would go completely unnoticed. As a rough guide it is best to size a cable to be thick enough so that at the average given current the voltage losses are no more than 5% of the nominal battery voltage (i.e. 0.6V max. for a 12 volt system).

In RE systems where the cable run from the power source may be long, or where the system voltage is low, the cable size must be chosen both to be big enough to carry the required current and to keep the voltage drop down to an acceptable level.

Durability

The other important factor in cable choice is durability. PVC covered 'twin core' cable is cheap and convenient for interior DC wiring, but even indoors should be protected from mechanical damage by careful routing or the use of conduits or cover strips. Multi-strand or flexible cable offers much better protection from conductor damage, and is essential in any situation where cables will experience movement. Outdoors, such cables should only be used fixed to walls where they are safe from mechanical damage, in cable ducts or fixed to an overhead strainer wire that carries the cable's weight. Since PVC degrades over time in sunlight, outside cabling can be protected by putting it inside black polyethylene water pipe. Steel-wire-armoured cable is considerably more expensive but is much preferred for outdoor use, and in most situations can be buried directly in the ground.

For high current battery circuits, single insulated conductors are often used. Flexible welding cable is ideal for potentially high currents. Battery cables should be protected from mechanical damage and the positive and negative conductors of each circuit should be kept close together to minimise stray electro-magnetic fields and circuit inductance.

Acceptable voltage drop

Excessive voltage drop over the length of your cables causes an unacceptable waste of energy. This may force the loads or power sources to work outside their optimum voltage range. At the least, this will reduce efficiency and at worst may cause permanent damage. Part of the skill in design work is to keep volt drop to a minimum within the cost constraints. An elegant design will produce an efficient system! The acceptable amount of voltage drop depends mainly on the system voltage. The same drop may be quite serious in 12V systems but negligible in 240V systems.

For copper cable in DC or single-phase AC circuits, the cable size needed to keep the voltage drop acceptable (under 5% of nominal voltage) can be estimated from the tables on pages 124-125. If your situation is not covered by the tables, use the formula:

volt drop (volts) = 0.04 x cable length (m) x current (amps) / cable cross-sectional area (mm^2)

$$\Delta V = 0.04 \, L \, I \, / \, A$$

Note that the 'length' is the length of one of the two conductors in the cable; the formula includes the effect of both conductors of a twin cable.

Power cabling losses

In small-scale RE systems, the most critical drop is usually on the cable from the power source, i.e. from the PV panel or the turbine. Keeping this distance to a minimum will affect the siting of wind turbines, PV panels and your battery store. How much the voltage drop affects the useful energy output of the PVs over a day or a month will depend on the type of PV and controller you are using, the weather conditions, and the load profile (i.e. when and for how long loads are switched on); see Fig. 8 .1. Modelling the system on

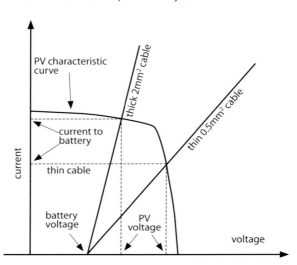

Fig. 8.1 Cable size and volt drop for a PV system

The power source efficiency of a system may suffer seriously if the voltage drop is too large. Consider the PV module in Case Study 2. In this case the drop adds to the battery voltage, increasing the voltage at the PV module. Let's assume that the battery is nearly charged with a terminal voltage of 13.5V, and that it is a hot sunny day (hot because that's when the crystalline PV source voltage is at its lowest). The graph above shows an example of a PV module current-voltage characteristic, together with the actual operating points under various conditions and for two different cable sizes. With the thin (or long) cable, the battery voltage plus the blocking-diode (Schottky type) volt drop plus the cable drop (which depends on the current) all add up to force the PV module to operate at a voltage that is too high for optimum power production. The cable sized for 20% power loss at nominal maximum power actually results in an overall loss of 31% under these conditions, i.e. only 69% of the power that the panel could produce actually reaches the battery. If a normal diode is used (rather than a low volt drop Schottky) and the battery is charged to say, 14.3V, the total loss could reach over 50% with the same cable. However, under most other operating conditions the loss would be much less than this.

Calculating the effects of volt drop on daily or monthly energy yield is difficult, so for simplicity it is best to err on the large side with your cable. If you size it for a 5% drop or less at maximum PV power and use a Schottky blocking diode rated for twice the maximum expected current, you won't go far wrong. The factor of 0.85 used in estimating the energy obtained from PVs is introduced to take account of these losses.

NB: some PV controllers incorporate a relay instead of a blocking diode to avoid this volt drop altogether. Check when doing your market survey.

a computer is probably only worthwhile for large and expensive systems, so for simplicity err on the large side with your cables – aim for a maximum of 5% loss at nominal Pmax (maximum PV power) – and you won't go far wrong.

Small battery-charging wind turbines are usually less affected by increased terminal voltage due to cable voltage drop, but if this is great it may mean that the machine never delivers full power, or only does so in very high winds. With some generators ('shunt field' types) permanent damage will be caused by operating at excessively high voltage.

The average percentage power loss in cables from a wind turbine or a PV panel (and therefore the percentage loss in annual energy production) is always considerably less than the percentage loss calculated at maximum power.

Wind turbines are generally best sited some distance away from buildings, and hence loads, to avoid turbulence and reduce noise disturbance. Where the distances involved will require unacceptably expensive cable sizes it may be preferable to consider turbines that generate at higher voltages, and either use a higher system voltage, or transmit high voltage AC direct from the turbine as far as the battery store before transforming and rectifying to the battery voltage.

Load voltage drops

The other limits on acceptable voltage drop are the maximum power-source voltage and the minimum acceptable load voltage. For example, 10% power loss on a cable feeding a low-voltage incandescent lamp may not at first sound too serious, but the reduced efficiency of the lamp caused by the low voltage will result in a total drop in light output of 25-30% rather than the 10% one might expect (see Fig. 6.5). Many fluorescent lamps are also voltage sensitive and may experience starting problems and reduced life if the voltage is too far below the rated value. A common problem with cheaper fluorescents running at low voltages is a tendency for the tubes to rapidly blacken, reducing light output and requiring replacement often within a few months of installation.

Rule of Thumb

A useful approximation for quick cable sizing for 12 volt systems is
Cable area (mm^2) ≈ Length (one way, m) x Current (A) ÷ 10
This gives a voltage drop of about 3.5%

e.g. You want to install a small light – 11W fluorescent – in an outhouse 35 metres from the battery store. At 12V, the light will draw about 1 amp.

cable size ≈ (1 x 35) / 10 = 3.5mm^2

The nearest available sizes are 2.5mm^2 and 4mm^2. If the light will be in constant use, perhaps as a security light, you should opt for the larger 4mm^2 to save power, but if it is only to be used occasionally, e.g. a garage light, the extra losses of a 2.5mm^2 cable may be worth the cost saving.

Cable size in a 12 volt system

Circuit watts up to:	Current up to:	Absolute minimum cable size	Minimum conductor area for less than 5% volt drop over given length			
			3m	10m	30m	100m
36W	3 amps	0.5mm^2	0.75mm^2	2.5mm^2	6mm^2	25mm^2
72W	6 amps	0.75mm^2	1.5mm^2	4mm^2	10mm^2	35mm^2
120W	10 amps	1.0mm^2	2.5mm^2	6mm^2	16mm^2	50mm^2
192W	16 amps	1.5mm^2	2.5mm^2	10mm^2	25mm^2	–
288W	24 amps	2.5mm^2	4.0mm^2	16mm^2	35mm^2	–
384W	32 amps	4mm^2	6mm^2	16mm^2	50mm^2	–
480W	40 amps	6mm^2	6mm^2	25mm^2	50mm^2	–

Cable size in a 24 volt system

Circuit watts up to:	Current up to:	Absolute minimum cable size	Minimum conductor area for less than 5% volt drop over given length			
			3m	10m	30m	100m
72W	3 amps	0.5mm^2	0.5mm^2	0.75mm^2	2.5mm^2	10mm^2
144W	6 amps	0.75mm^2	0.75mm^2	1.5mm^2	4mm^2	16mm^2
240W	10 amps	1.0mm^2	1mm^2	2.5mm^2	10mm^2	25mm^2
384W	16 amps	1.5mm^2	1.5mm^2	4mm^2	16mm^2	50mm^2
576W	24 amps	2.5mm^2	2.5mm^2	6mm^2	25mm^2	–
768W	32 amps	4mm^2	4mm^2	10mm^2	25mm^2	–
960W	40 amps	6mm^2	6mm^2	10mm^2	35mm^2	–

Cable size in a 240 volt system

Circuit power up to:	Current up to:	Absolute minimum area	Minimum conductor area for less than 5% volt drop over given length			
			20m	50m	100m	200m
0.7kW	3 amps	0.5mm²	0.5mm²	0.5mm²	1mm²	2.5mm²
1.4kW	6 amps	0.75mm²	0.75mm²	1mm²	2.5mm²	4mm²
2.4kW	10 amps	1mm²	1mm²	2.5mm²	4mm²	10mm²
3.4kW	14 amps	1.5mm²	1mm²	2.5mm²	6mm²	10mm²
5.8kW	24 amps	2.5mm²	2.5mm²	4mm²	10mm²	16mm²
7.7kW	32 amps	4mm²	4mm²	6mm²	16mm²	–

Electrical safety

The electrical installation of RE systems mostly follows standard wiring practice. Information on standard domestic wiring is widely available in books and DIY manuals, so we won't cover this here. There are, however, important ways in which RE wiring differs from standard practice. Most small RE systems use low voltage DC (12 or 24V) rather than, or as well as, the normal 240V AC and this has several implications.

There is very little danger of electric shock with low voltage systems, but other hazards are still there and some new ones appear. Electrical fires are perhaps the worst potential problem, and are usually caused by excessive current or faulty appliances. All cables must be properly sized and protected by fuses, just as in a mains system. Other risks such as arcing switch contacts and potentially explosive battery gases arise, and must be taken seriously. The IEE 'On-Site' guide gives useful guidance on cable sizing and protective devices (see Resources).

If you are not sure of your competence, get a qualified electrician to do the job or to advise you, as inadequate RE installations can be just as dangerous as a mains-powered one. In any case, when completed, your entire system should be checked by an accredited electrician.

Cable rating

Typical storage batteries are capable of supplying enough current to melt almost any cable! The fire hazard is therefore particularly

125

significant. Do not fall into the trap of thinking, 'It's only 12 volts; this bit of thin flex will do!' The low voltage means that you will usually need thicker cable, and it must be protected upstream by a fuse or circuit breakers (MCB) rated at less than or equal to the cable's safe operating current – don't just rely on the main battery fuse. This applies even to low-power lamps, meter sense wires and powered meters.

PV power cables should be rated for at least 1.25 times the array short circuit current. If you expect reflected light from water or snow leave a bigger margin. Wind and hydro generator cables should tolerate at least twice the current at maximum power. With battery and load cables, it makes sense to size them with plenty of potential for expansion, and for at least twice maximum expected current. Remember that inverters can sometimes draw three times their rated current for short surge loads.

Switches

DC systems have an additional fire hazard – their high potential for maintained arcing of switches, thermostats and relay contacts. In AC systems the arc (spark) which occurs when contacts open is usually extinguished very quickly. However, DC tends to maintain the arc – in some cases (e.g. an AC thermostat operating on DC it may continue until the arc's heat has melted the whole appliance and perhaps started a fire! The problem is much worse with higher voltage DC systems (say, 48 volts and above) where only special DC rated switches, thermostats and relay contacts should be used. At 12 or 24 volts DC many switches and relays rated for 240V AC are safe, provided that they are well within their current rating, preferably operating under half the AC rated current.

Disconnects

Having worked out how to join all the components of the system together, you also need to consider how to disconnect them. Working on a system with live wires floating around can result in spectacular mishaps. There are several reasons you might want to isolate parts of a system:
- maintenance and repair;
- adding new wiring or equipment;

• replacing fuses;
• isolating and testing faults;
• emergency shutdown.

You should be able to disconnect all loads, the batteries, and each power source individually – see Fig. 8.2. With small systems up to 100 or 200 watts, the circuit breakers or pull-out fuses (rather than the bolted type) fitted for over-current protection can be used. For larger systems, use dedicated isolating switches, rated for DC and the operating voltage and current – in some countries such as the US this is a legal requirement. Mount all the isolators together and clearly label them so that it is easy to shut everything down in an emergency. AC lines from inverters and gensets also need isolators in accordance with mains wiring standards, but AC and DC cables should not share conduit or distribution boxes.

If the system negative is not earthed you should use double pole isolators to disconnect both positive and negative, but earthed conductors should not be switchable. Wind and hydro generators should never be disconnected from their dump loads unless they have been 'parked'. Shorting the output cables is an effective way to lock most wind generators, but don't try it in high winds unless you enjoy fireworks.

Over current protection

As we have already seen, current passing down a wire makes heat. Too much current will melt it, and possibly cause a fire. Over current can be the result of a fault, such as a short circuit, or overload. Either way all circuits carrying power to and from batteries must be protected against over current by fuses or MCBs close to the battery. Make sure the fuses and MCBs are rated for DC use – they should blow at or below the cable's rated maximum current. The same protection is, of course, needed at higher working voltages; with normal mains appliances in the UK, it is provided by fitting a suitably rated fuse in the mains plug, as well as general circuit protection with MCBs in the distribution box.

AC waveforms

The voltage output waveform of many inverters and AC load controllers often used on micro-hydro systems is not smooth sine wave like the normal mains supply. This can cause problems with RCCBs and sometimes with fuse and MCB ratings. Consult an electrical engineer if in doubt! Such non-sinusoidal waveforms can also cause dangerous overheating of certain appliances – check carefully before leaving anything unattended.

Lightning

All electrical installations are susceptible to damage and hazard due to lightning, particularly overhead distribution systems in rural areas. RE systems with long overhead cable runs and/or wind turbines are most vulnerable, and proper lightning protection should always be fitted. Even then, a direct hit will cause trouble. The main defences are:

- very comprehensive earthing at the wind turbine or other remote power source, and at the battery negative terminal;
- a lightning trap (spark gap or varistor) on the cable before it enters a building;
- fitting lightning spikes above vulnerable components.

For long cables (over 20m) in lightning prone areas, it is a good

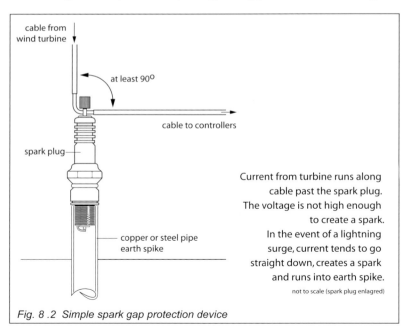

Fig. 8 .2 Simple spark gap protection device

idea to enclose them in metal conduit (or use armoured cable) earthed at several points to minimise induced surges in the cable. Protection against moderate over-voltage surges, such as varistors or 'crowbar' circuits, should be provided as a matter of course in electronic controls connected to any RE system (see Chapter 7, Controling and Monitoring Your System).

Simple spark gap protectors, particularly suitable for small wind generators, can be made using old petrol engine spark plugs (see Fig. 8.2). During normal operation, current bypasses the plugs, but when high voltage spikes occur, current jumps across the spark gap and is safely earthed.

Electric shocks

There is hardly any electric shock hazard from purely low voltage (12/24V) DC systems. However, many power sources have the potential to create hazardous voltages, especially when disconnected from a battery bank. Most nominally 12 volt PV modules produce open circuit voltages well over 20V. Systems using several PVs connected in series can easily produce dangerous voltages before they are connected to the batteries. To avoid this hazard cover the array with a blanket until the connections are made.

Hydro sites in particular often mix quite high voltages with cramped, damp and solitary working conditions in the turbine shed – all of which increase the hazard level. For similar reasons, even more care is needed to avoid possible electric shock hazards when working up wind turbine towers. Even some 12 volt wind turbines can give high voltages (as much as 150V – quite enough for a nasty shock if they operate disconnected from the battery).

High voltage DC is best avoided, certainly in the domestic setting, as it presents considerably worse shock hazard than similar AC voltage.

Any system incorporating an inverter or generating 240V AC must include protection from electric shock by:
- proper insulation of all live parts;
- thorough earthing of all metal parts which could contact live parts (thus limiting the dangerous voltage and blowing the fuse or trip if a fault occurs);
- the use of earth leakage trips such as RCCBs.

Earthing

Earthing involves making an electrical link between parts of the system and the ground. In all systems, mounting structures should be earthed, and in larger systems, it is accepted practice to earth the battery negative and inverters. Any exposed metal on appliances operating above 24 volts should also be earthed.

The main reason for earthing is safety. If a fault occurs in an unearthed appliance the casing may become 'live'. If the supply is earthed, when you touch the casing your body will make an ideal path for current to flow to the earth – a hair raising experience. If the casing is earthed, current will flow as soon as the fault occurs, hopefully blowing the circuit fuse or breaker. Earthing also dissipates static and induced voltage surges, reduces lightning risk and minimises radio interference from fluorescent lights.

In most situations, an earth rod, typically galvanised steel, 1.5 to 2 metres long, is driven into the ground to make the earthing point. Bare or insulated copper conductors link appliances and the battery negative to the rod – the conductor should be at least as thick as the largest conductor in the circuit supplying the earthed device. If there is more than one earth rod, the rods should be linked together to prevent hazardous potential differences occurring.

All wind turbine towers and PV and hydro mounting frames should have their own earthing point, linked by a short, thick cable with as few bends as possible in order to provide some protection from lightning (see Fig. 8.3).

System installation

Many small renewable energy systems can be successfully installed by practical amateurs with a range of DIY and electrical skills. Activities that may require professional assistance include the erection of larger wind turbines (300W or more), the installation of hydro-electric generators and the commissioning of more complex systems.

If you are having your system professionally installed there are often many small jobs that you can do beforehand to save costs, such as digging trenches for buried cable runs and foundations – consult your installers to find out what you can do to help.

You will need to get an electrician to check the system and

make the final connections in order to avoid potentially expensive and hazardous mistakes and to comply with Part P of Building Regulations. This is essential if the system includes an inverter or any other 240V source.

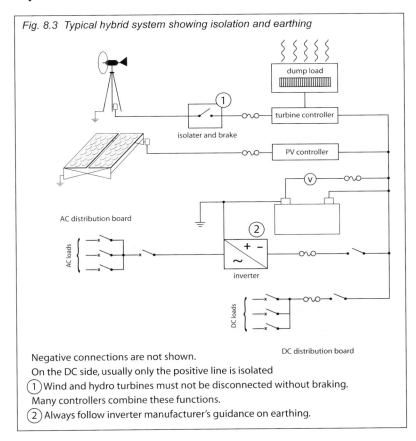

Fig. 8.3 Typical hybrid system showing isolation and earthing

dump load

turbine controller

isolater and brake

PV controller

AC distribution board

AC loads

inverter

DC loads

DC distribution board

Negative connections are not shown.
On the DC side, usually only the positive line is isolated
① Wind and hydro turbines must not be disconnected without braking.
Many controllers combine these functions.
② Always follow inverter manufacturer's guidance on earthing.

Preparation

The key to a hassle-free installation is to prepare the equipment, materials and tools required beforehand.

Design

You should have a detailed circuit diagram for the whole system, and a plan of the wiring layout that you will have used to work out cable runs and voltage drops. When siting various elements such as PV arrays, wind turbines and battery stores, consider the

A small wind turbine on a guyed tower is erected in South Africa using a gin pole.

implications in terms of delivery and mounting of components, cable routing and fixing, and any special equipment required, e.g. roof ladders, extra long masonry bits, winches, etc. Once you have a detailed design, make a complete list of all the components and materials that will be needed.

Components

Ensure that you have all the ingredients on your design list on site. Make sure you have enough cable and sundry items such as connector blocks, insulation tape and cable clips. Since most off-grid power systems are in remote locations, it can be very frustrating and costly to have to stop half way through an installation to fetch a few overlooked screws from a distant hardware store. Also check that you have read the installation instructions for all the system components.

Safety

System installation involves hazardous equipment and activities that require particular care to avoid accidents. Wear appropriate clothing and keep a first aid kit handy. Do not work alone – have at least one assistant to help with lifting, ladders, the inevitable 'three-hand' jobs, and in case of accidents.

Batteries

These contain sulphuric acid so must be transported and handled with great care. Keep some sodium bicarbonate handy to neutralise spills, or purchase a dedicated battery acid spill kit. Wear rubber gloves, goggles, boots and a plastic apron when moving vented batteries. They tend to be heavy, so take care not to hurt your back when lifting them – lift from underneath or with handles, not by the terminals. Do NOT smoke near batteries as they give off explosive hydrogen gas. When connecting up battery strings, take special care not to short the terminals with tools – covering spanner handles with insulation tape can prevent spectacular accidents. Battery stores should be identified with clear and appropriate safety and warning signs.

Working above ground

Take particular care when mounting PV arrays on roofs. Use a roofing ladder to provide a firm footing and spread your weight, and use safety ropes for yourself and the panels to prevent calamitous drops. Everyone in the immediate vicinity should wear hard hats to protect against falling tools and tiles. Tool belts are invaluable for keeping tools secure but convenient.

Extreme caution is necessary when working up wind turbine towers. Avoid it if possible, or leave it to the experts. It is much safer to lower the tower using a gin-pole and make adjustments on the ground. If you must go aloft, wait for calm conditions and use a climbing harness, safety rope and helmet. Stop or slow the turbine from the ground by furling it or shorting the output wires (but not during high winds).

Electric shocks

Nominally low voltage wind turbines and PV arrays connected in series can produce hazardous voltages when disconnected from the battery bank. Use a rope to tether the turbine and cover PVs with a blanket until connected. Hydro systems generating 240V should be commissioned by experienced technicians and engineers.

To reduce electrical risks, take special care to check the polarity is correct and there are no short circuits before connecting components. Label cables as you work to aid final connections. Ensure that module frames, mountings, turbine towers, inverters and the battery negative terminal are all securely connected through suitably thick earth wires to an earth spike (a spike is temporary and a rod a permanent fixture).

Tools

Make sure you have all the tools you need before you start. These will probably include:

Screwdrivers – large and small, flat and cross

Wire cutters and stripper

Crimping tool

12V or gas soldering iron

12V hammer drill, high speed steel and masonry bits

Multimeter

Compass and protractor / inclinometer

Spirit level

Tape measure

Pliers

Adjustable spanner

Socket set

Spanners

Hacksaw

Knife

Hammer

Masonry chisel

Torch

Ladder

Safety rope and harness

Procedure

Loads

• Mount light fittings, sockets, switches, junction boxes and conduit
• Wire up, ensuring correct colour coding and sound connections

Batteries

• Mount and secure in racks
• Interconnect terminals to achieve desired voltage and ampacity (amp-hour capacity)
• Check electrolyte levels and state of charge
• Cover terminals
• Fit battery fuse

Materials
Cables
Earth wire and rod
Conduit and fittings
Junction boxes
Insulation tape
Cable clips and ties
Silicon sealant
Connector blocks
Crimp lugs
Wall plugs and bolts
Screws, nails, nuts, bolts, washers
Grease
Paint
Filling plaster

Sources
• Lay power cables
• Mount and interconnect PV arrays – cover with blanket
• Erect wind turbines and lock off guy shackles and turnbuckles with wire
• Earth module frames, mountings and turbine tower

Controllers and protection
• Mount controller/s, meters, fuses and distribution board
• Fit earth spike

Double check
• Check polarity of battery cables, power sources and sensitive loads such as fluorescent lights and inverters
• Check open circuit voltage and short circuit current of PV array (remove blanket and measure during daylight – replace blanket before final connection)
• Check that all loads are switched off
• Get an electrician to check everything, particularly any AC wiring

Final connections
• Connect battery to controller, negative first – check for 'on' indicator

- Connect loads to distribution board and controller
- Connect sources to controllers
- Remove blanket from PVs and tether from wind turbines
  – check for 'charging' indicator on controller/s

Commission system
- Check indicator lights on the controller are functioning as expected
- Check and record any meter readings
- Check that all loads work satisfactorily
- Check voltage drops at furthest points whilst all loads are on
- Check that all users understand implications of controller indicators and meter readings, and what to do in the event of a breakdown

Maintenance schedule
- Keep a log book documenting system performance and maintenance
- Work out a calendar of regular and long term maintenance tasks, e.g. battery voltage – daily, electrolyte level – monthly, wind turbine greasing – annually
- Display basic instructions by the control board in case inexperienced users have to check for simple faults like fuses and low voltage disconnections

Chapter 9
Mobile Systems

This mobile home gets both DC and AC power from several PV modules and a small wind turbine.

There is growing interest in the use of renewable energy for mobile homes, boats and outdoor events. Given the wide availability in UK of grid connection, mobile users are probably the largest potential market for off-grid domestic power supplies. There are two main categories of mobile loads:

Domestic – providing lights, music and entertainment, portable computers and phones, and low power tools.

Outdoor events – sound systems, lighting and small appliances for food and trading stalls.

The design procedures are similar to those for static systems, but there are other criteria important in mobile systems that need to be considered. Key amongst these are portability, safety and durability. In the case of marine systems, resistance to corrosion is also essential.

Batteries

Sealed cells are far safer than vented cells which can spill acid in a rolling boat or bouncing truck. If you do use vented cells, make sure that potential leaks can be safely contained e.g. by a rubber tray, and keep a supply of a mild alkali such as sodium carbonate (or caustic soda) handy to neutralise any spills. Despite their inherent risks, thick plate vented cells are generally more tolerant of the knocks and jolts that occur in road transport than sealed cells, particularly the gel type. Some deep-cycle vented cells are supplied with recombination caps that reduce the loss of electrolyte and greatly reduce the risk of spillage. For outdoor event systems, large battery banks weighing half a tonne or more may be required, with serious implications for transport and handling. It is best to mount the batteries permanently in the truck or a trailer to avoid handling hazards.

Energy Resources

Since the systems are on the move, potential resources are far harder to estimate. A reasonable guess can be made for solar insolation but availability may be seriously compromised by shading from buildings and trees. Wind is almost impossible to predict, but it is fair to assume that a good park-up site will be somewhat sheltered and hence far from ideal for a wind turbine. At events, 'people power' is a useful and plentiful resource. Pedal generators are an ideal mobile back-up as they will be available as long as there are willing pedallers around. In general, a mix of power sources and a willingness to tailor loads to available supply are required. Whatever the sources, they need to be robust and compact, and, for vehicle-based systems, quick, simple and flexible to erect.

Split charging

An advantage with mobile systems is that the domestic battery can be recharged quickly by connecting to the engine powered charging circuit for the starter motor battery. However, it is important to separate the two so that power can feed into the domestic battery

A bank of secondhand sealed batteries and control board supplying power at a festival.

but cannot be drawn back to supply the starter motor as the high currents involved can damage deep-cycle batteries. Similarly, it prevents the starter battery being flattened by the domestic load. There are several ways to achieve this one-way connection.

The first approach is to connect large heat sink-mounted diodes (150-200 amp) on the positive alternator output to each battery. A disadvantage with this approach is that due to the voltage drop across the diode (0.3 to 1 volt depending on type), the alternator's automatic voltage regulator (AVR) will curtail the charging current before the batteries are full. This effect can be minimised by using a large (say, 100 amp rating) Schottky diode that will only drop 0.3V at the currents involved, or by adjusting the AVR to increase its maximum voltage by the amount dropped across the diode, e.g. to 14.5V for a diode drop of 0.8-1.0V. This arrangement ensures even charging of both batteries but prevents either feeding the other's loads. Pre-mounted diode sets are available commercially for this purpose.

For the less auto-electrically adventurous, the other approach is probably the simplest, and entails fitting a large relay to the output of the alternator. The relay is activated when the alternator starts to charge once the engine is running. Suitable relays designed for this purpose are available from caravan supply outlets for about £16 and can also provide a separate supply to run a 12V fridge direct from the alternator whilst the engine is running. When the engine stops, the two batteries are effectively isolated.

Although it is common practice to earth the negative battery terminal in an off-grid system, do NOT do this if you are using a split charger on an old vehicle with positive earth wiring.

Charging currents

Vehicle alternators can produce currents as high as 100 amps when charging a flat battery. Although most batteries can cope with short bursts of high current up to C Amps (where C is the amp-hour capacity rating), deep-cycle batteries do not appreciate prolonged fast charging, preferring rates in the order of C/10 amps. Most sealed batteries, especially the type designed for float applications such as uninterruptible power supplies, are particularly sensitive to high currents – check with the manufacturer for the maximum safe current. The charging current can be limited by adding a high power, low resistance in series with the battery. If the domestic battery is several metres from the alternator, the resistance of the cable may be sufficient. As a rough guide, the limiting resistance should be in the order of 2/I ohms where I is the maximum current required, and rated for at least 2xI watts power dissipation. For example, if the current requires limiting to 20A, the resistance needed will be 2/20 = 0.1 Ω, with a power rating >40W. Copper cables have a resistance given by the formula:

Resistance(Ω) = 0.04 x Length (m, one way) / Cable Area (mm^2)

Thus, if the battery supply cable is 7 metres long each way and 4mm^2 in area, it will have a resistance of 7 x 0.04 / 4 = 0.07Ω in which case the cable alone should limit the current to 29A.

Photovoltaics

Crystalline modules are better for mobile systems than less efficient amorphous panels, which take up nearly twice as much space to generate the same amount of power and are heavier to transport. Small amorphous modules are sometimes available at festivals for about £50 for 10Wp (peak watts) but their output tends to drop significantly after a few years' use. The latest 'multi-junction' amorphous panels have a better life, whilst crystalline modules often have their output guaranteed for at least 10 years. Crystalline modules with outputs in the region of 40 to 80Wp cost about £4 per peak watt, representing the best investment if you can afford them.

The simplest mounting arrangement is to prop the module(s) in a suitably sunny position attached to a trailing lead, but this is vulnerable to damage and theft. It is better to mount them on the vehicle roof, if possible using a mounting that can swivel for optimum orientation without having to manoeuvre the whole vehicle. A simple method for one or two panels is attach them to a single pole with a simple frame hinged at the top with an adjustable brace at the bottom to adjust the tilt-angle to suit the season and allow for easy storage.

The ultimate mobile solar sound system, designed for renewable buskers.

Wind turbines

The energy available from the wind is far less predictable since good park-up sites are often sheltered. The presence of trees, buildings and other vehicles will create significant turbulence. Boats are more likely to be exposed to better wind resources. Small turbines up to 1 metre in diameter such as those available from Marlec, Ampair and LMW are suitably compact and lightweight. Several are available in marine models – with short tails and improved corrosion resistance. On boats, these can be mounted semi-permanently off the stern, 1 to 3 metres above the deck, but they should be dismountable in the event of extreme weather conditions. On land, turbines can be mounted on a removable pole such as a length of 2 inch water pipe or scaffold, attached to the corner of the vehicle and projecting at least 3 to 4 metres above the roof. For longer stays, a separate, taller, guyed mast will give better results. It is worth noting that a tower attached to the vehicle will transmit some vibration and noise into the vehicle body.

Pedal generators

For a domestic system, a home-made pedal generator can provide a useful emergency back-up supply for cloudy, windless days. Plans are available from Campaign for Real Events (see Resources) for a simple car alternator version that can produce 60 to 100W. Higher efficiency multi-pole generators will reduce the gearing required and give better output. The ideal pedalling speed is around 60–100rpm. As an alternative to building a dedicated frame, it may be possible to adapt a normal bicycle on a stand with a belt running off a tyreless rear wheel, or to modify an exercise cycle.

Inverter-chargers

If you are thinking of using an inverter to provide 230V AC power, it is worth considering one with a built in battery charging facility ('standby option'). Many marinas and caravan sites provide grid power connections which may be used, at a cost, to recharge low battery banks. Petrol-powered battery chargers are also available from caravan supplies outlets, but are far less versatile than either a small 230V AC generator or an inverter charger since they give no AC output.

Leeds AT's mobile power system at the renewably-powered festival, the Big Green Gathering. The left hand hatch houses DC input, control and output to loads like phone chargers and a portable stereo, whilst the right panel is for the inverter and AC loads such as hair clippers.

Cabling and protection

As with any low-voltage system, cables must be sized to minimise voltage drops (see Chapter 8). Since distances within a vehicle or boat are fairly small, it is worth considering ring circuits similar to those used in standard domestic wiring practice, as these can halve losses without having to use more cumbersome, thicker cable. The supply cable runs in a loop after the fuse and loads are connected in parallel between positive and negative conductors.

Correctly sized fuses are essential, especially on a boat where an electrical fire could be catastrophic. Use separately fused circuits for lights, stereo, 12V appliances and, if used, inverter, the output of which should be protected by a residual current device and more fuses or MCBs. In general, inverters should be earthed to the vehicle body since without an earth connection, RCDs and ELCBs will not work. However, check the manufacturer's instructions first. If a vehicle is stationary, it is best to connect the earth to a temporary earth-spike such as a copper-coated or galvanised rod or pipe hammered into the ground.

Some inverters have an internal link between earth and negative. If you have an old vehicle wired positive earth it is best not to attempt to use both an alternator split charger and an inverter as there is a chance of a potentially dangerous short circuit developing.

Domestic systems

These are typically fairly small in the region of 100W peak load, providing a few lights, stereo, and perhaps a small 12V TV, mobile phone and portable computer. A small inverter (100-600W) could be added for short term AC loads such as small power tools. 12V fridges are available but significantly increase load. Thermal fridges that run off LPG, 12V DC and 230V AC are far less efficient than compressor types, but are more versatile as LPG will often already be used for cooking. Caravan supplies outlets usually stock such items – a typical 70 litre model uses about 2.3kWh (190Ahr at 12V) per day, depending on thermostat setting, ambient temperature and frequency of opening and loading. This is uneconomic for full time 12V renewable supply – in contrast, a 100 litre high efficiency DC compressor fridge uses about 600Wh. However, if the fridge is frequently running directly from the alternator when travelling, and partly from gas when stationary, its remaining load on the 12V system can be reduced by increasing insulation around the cabinet, and storing bottles of water (frozen ones are best) as a thermal flywheel (store of 'coolth').

It is important to use a separate battery for the domestic loads as vehicle batteries do not perform well in deep-cycling applications and if flattened by over-use will be incapable of starting the vehicle.

Non-domestic systems

Outdoor events are usually 'off-grid' and rely on large, hired diesel generators. There is increasing interest in smaller, renewable power supplies on the festival circuit. There are a growing number of such rigs that run lights, small sound systems, cinemas, circuses and other low power loads such as mobile phones and hair clippers. Many of these groups have systems that can be hired for events – see Resources.

If you are considering setting up your own rig, the design process is similar to that for the other systems described, bearing in mind the influence of portability and prolonged loads imposed by all night use. The key phrases are 'low power' and 'high efficiency'. Small-scale renewable energy supplies are not cost-effective for some applications such as large sound systems (1kW +), high-tech lighting rigs, chest freezers, kettles or urns. However, much can be achieved with very little power. A four person pedal generator can keep 200 people dancing all night and 150 watts of halogen and fluorescent lights, LED strings (see Chapter 5) and a low-power strobe can turn a small marquee into a psychedelic grotto.

Wind and solar power are now a common sight at many festivals.

Public safety

All the safety guidance provided in this book is applicable to outdoor entertainment systems, but operators should be even more careful since they will be legally responsible should a member of the public be hurt by a fault. Particular care should be taken to exclude the public from the vicinity of batteries, distribution boards, PV modules and low-mounted wind turbines. Wind turbines on free standing towers require a drop zone around the turbine with a radius greater than the height of the tower. Guys and pegs should be marked as hazards and cables should be slit-trenched or kept out of reach. Do not forget to earth your system, particularly if it incorporates AC. Ask event organisers whether you are covered by their public liability insurance.

It is worth noting that systems running entirely on voltages below 50V are classified in I.E.C. Safety Regulations as 'Extra Low Voltage Temporary Installations' and require no special precautions with cabling other than prevention of obstruction. Higher voltage systems, such as those running inverters, are required by Environmental Health regulations to keep all supply cables two feet underground or 20 feet overhead. In practice, this rarely occurs, leaving operators potentially liable should any accidents occur. At the very least, outdoor cables should be slit-trenched and those indoors kept well off the ground wherever possible. DC and AC cabling should be kept separate and should be adequately identified. All AC supplies must be protected by Residual Current Devices, as well as over-current trips or fuses.

Sound systems

Pedal generators are ideally suited to mobile sound systems as the punters provide their own power all night, and remove the need for large and costly battery banks. Larger wind turbines on exposed sites are also effective. Since sound systems are often used at night, solar-based systems require massive and hazardous battery banks to store enough energy from the daytime.

Recent developments in digital amplifier technology offer significant improvements in efficiency, especially for bass speakers, which consume the bulk of the energy required to run a sound system.

There are three main supply options, which may be combined or used separately.

230V AC Inverters can be connected to a battery bank and used to run conventional PA systems. This requires no special adaptation of the sound equipment, which can be hired from normal suppliers. However, there are several problems that make this the least suitable for all but the most occasional users. Even high quality inverters are inefficient when running variable loads like amplifiers, and the losses are doubled inside the amp where the 230V AC is re-converted back to low and medium voltage DC. Because of these

A pedal powered sound system and stage lights.

losses, AC-based systems require considerably more power than DC systems to produce similar results. In addition, the square or modified square-wave output (see Chapter 5 – Inverters) of many inverters can create annoying hums or buzzes in the amplifiers. The use of 230V AC creates many potential hazards, especially in outdoor applications where their use is governed by stringent electrical safety standards. It is essential that such installations should include Residual Current Devices to minimise the risk of electrical shocks.

24 to 100V DC supplies are becoming increasingly popular with pedal-based sound systems. Many PA amplifiers operate internally on ±50V DC, and by supplying the power rails direct, significant improvements in efficiency are achieved. Multi-pole, permanent magnet alternators designed specifically for pedal generators can be adapted to feed a 96V battery bank. The centre (48V) is connected to the amplifier's zero rail (or casing if no other fixing is apparent), and the two extremes then provide plus and minus 48V to drive the amplifier. The high supply voltage offers advantages in terms of reduced cable losses, but creates a potentially lethal hazard. Such a supply requires specialised trips and switch-gear which are harder to find than those for 230V AC or 12V DC. This option should only be considered by those familiar with electronics and electrical installation because of the complexities and risks involved.

A four-person permanent magnet pedal generator keeps the sounds pumping.

It is worth noting that the internal circuitry of most simple power amplifiers will happily operate off any plus/minus voltage between 12V and that normally supplied by the built-in power supply, provided the positive and negative rails are balanced. At lower voltages, output volume will have to be drastically reduced to prevent 'clipping' and distortion. Since the power is proportional to the square of the supply voltage, halving the battery bank voltage, say from ±48V to ±24V, will quarter the output power, whilst cable losses will be increased fourfold.

12V DC systems are by far the safest option but require dedicated equipment, some electronic skills to build, and are more suited to smaller rigs up to 200W r.m.s. Large car amplifiers can provide this level of output and some tape decks and turntables can be run on 12V by bypassing the AC transformers and rectifiers. Low power DC converters can be made from relatively cheap components to power mixing desks and effects pedals. For rough sizing purposes, the continuous input power will be about one third of the peak power plus that required to run desks and decks. An excellent guide to DIY 12 Volt sound systems is available from the Campaign for Real Events (see Resources).

Case study 1
Hydro System

Mr and Mrs Brook and their four children were searching for a new home in the countryside. They decided to look for a remote property without a mains connection, as such properties are often quite cheap, allowing them to have a large house on a fairly limited income. They planned to use a diesel generator in the short term, then install an RE system when they could afford it.

Mrs Brook is a freelance writer and requires a reliable electricity supply for her word processor, printer, and fax machine. Also, with a large family, the Brooks were not prepared to do without the usual domestic appliances such as a fridge, toaster, kettle, television, and video. Fortunately, before they selected which property to buy, they began researching renewable energy.

After seeking advice they drew up a list of all their loads, found out their size and estimated how many hours they would be using in a average day. You can see the result below.

The table reveals three things. Firstly, the Brooks' system must be able to generate 7185Wh of energy on average each day. Secondly, in order to be able to power the kettle and a few lights, it must be able to provide around 2kW of power. If it is necessary to run the kettle and the toaster at the same time, nearer 3kW will be needed. Thirdly, if a site with enough energy but not enough peak power were available, batteries could be used to collect energy over the whole day then provide the peak power required via a suitable sized inverter. This could reduce the required power output to around 300W over the whole 24 hours.

To provide these power and energy needs the Brooks decided to try to find a property with hydro-power potential, as this would be the easiest and cheapest way of providing for their high-power needs, such as the kettle and toaster. The Brooks were wise in that they decided to examine their energy needs before they chose their property. This allowed them to search for a site suitable for a hydro-power scheme. Hydro-power is

The Brooks work out their electrical load needs

Appliance	Wattage	Number	Hours use/day	Total Wh/day
1 Word processor	100	1	8	800
2 Printer	50	1	1	50
3 Fax machine	60	1	0.5	30
4 Kettle	1500	1	1	1500
5 Toaster	1000	1	0.25	250
6 Fridge	100	1	24	2400
7 Television	100 (av.)	1	4	400
8 Video	120	1	2	240
9 Lights	60	6	4	1440
10 Spin Drier	300	1	0.25	75
11 Max. power required (= number times wattage, totalled)				3690W
12 Total energy required per day				7185Wh/day
13 Average power required (per hour: row 12 divided by 24)				300W

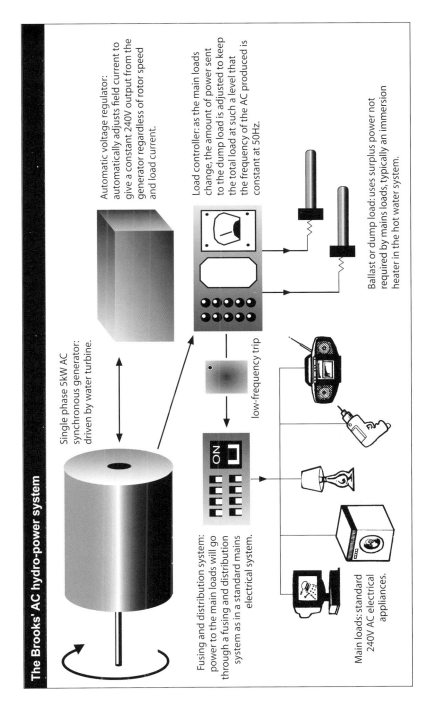

The Brooks' AC hydro-power system

Automatic voltage regulator: automatically adjusts field current to give a constant 240V output from the generator regardless of rotor speed and load current.

Load controller: as the main loads change, the amount of power sent to the dump load is adjusted to keep the total load at such a level that the frequency of the AC produced is constant at 50Hz.

Ballast or dump load: uses surplus power not required by mains loads, typically an immersion heater in the hot water system.

Single phase 5kW AC synchronous generator: driven by water turbine.

low-frequency trip

Fusing and distribution system: power to the main loads will go through a fusing and distribution system as in a standard mains electrical system.

Main loads: standard 240V AC electrical appliances.

often the cheapest and most reliable type of RE system, but it is very site specific.

After looking at several sites, the Brooks finally found a property in North Yorkshire, with an estimated flow rate of 0.06m3 per second and a head of 15m. It had potential for a 5kW direct AC hydro scheme that would more than satisfy their maximum power and energy needs, with enough left over to make a significant contribution to their background heating via the dump load. At this power level there is no need for battery storage, so no need to consider DC.

If a sufficient water resource for continuous operation is ever available, a direct AC system such as this removes the expense and inefficiencies incurred with a battery storage type system.

For the first year they used a 3kW diesel generator. Then, with the help of a renewable energy company, they installed their hydro system. The system costs were reduced considerably by the Brooks doing the straightforward labour-intensive tasks themselves (such as digging the hole for the intake and trenches for cables and pipes) while the experts did the really complex bits.

Case study 2
Wind/Solar Hybrid System

Tom and Sarah Breeze and their daughter Gale bought a remote cottage in west Wales in 1988 and had been running it on a diesel generator. In 1994 the noise and fumes from their diesel generator finally drove them to investigate the alternatives. The cost of grid connection was £12,000, so Sarah Breeze talked to engineers at CAT (sensible person!) to see what options were available. A quick survey of the location ruled out the possibility of a hydro-power scheme: there was no nearby stream. However, the upland location made a wind system look like the most likely option, perhaps with some photovoltaics to help them through the calmer summer months.

As the Breeze family were living on a fairly low income obtained from their family business, Sarah asked how the system costs could be kept to a minimum. She was advised to buy a renewable energy system sized to meet the average load from their television, lights, hi-fi, sewing machine, and other low-power appliances. The occasional use of high-power appliances such as washing machines and power tools could be achieved by running the diesel generator as and when required. When the diesel is running, it could also be used to top up the batteries at the same time. Cutting down their electricity consumption would reduce the cost of their RE system from around £12,000, for a system to completely meet all of their energy needs from renewables, to around £2,000 for a system designed to meet their reduced load.

To get a wind turbine away from the wind disturbances caused by the building and by some trees lower down the hillside, it would probably be necessary to place it about 100 metres uphill from the cottage. Although the cottage roof faced east-west, there was a lean-to on one end facing due south. This would be an ideal place for PVs, as it had an unobstructed view right round from east to west and a south-facing slope of about 30° to the horizontal.

Off The Grid

The Breeze's energy requirements: option 1 – cutting back

	Appliance	LOAD AC/DC	Number in use	Power watts	TIME Summer hrs/day	watt-hrs/day energy consumed	TIME Winter hrs/day	watt-hrs/day energy consumed
1	Low-energy lights	DC	1	16	x 5	= 80	x 8	= 128
2	Low-energy lights	DC	2	8	x 5	= 80	x 5	= 80
3	B/W portable TV	DC	1	12	x 3	= 36	x 5	= 60
4	Car type stereo system	DC	1	5 (av.)	x 3	= 15	x 5	= 25
5	**dc load consumption**					**211**		**293**
6	Sewing machine (1 hr/wk)	AC	1	50	x 0.14	= 7	x 0.14	= 7
7	Allowance for inverter losses* (approx. 20% of load)					1.4		1.4
8	Input energy to inverter					8.4		8.4
9	**Total dc consumption** (rows 5+8)					**219.4**		**301.4**
10	Allowances for battery losses (approx. 25% of load)					54.9		75.4
11	**Input energy to battery required per day** (rows 9 + 10)					**274.3**		**376.8**
12	Average power input (watt-hours per day divided by 24) (row 11/24)					11.4W		15.7W

* The inverter is only running when the sewing machine is in use, so there are no standby losses to account for, just the efficiency figure, assumed to be around 83%.

154

As Sarah and Tom could not decide there and then on how much electricity they would need, they drew up two options. Option 1, where they cut down consumption to the minimum that they felt they could live with; and Option 2, where they allowed for more appliance use, and for less careful use of lighting.

To discover their loads in each case, they made two lists of their power requirements in watts and the estimated average number of hours they would need to run each low-power appliance each day. Examine the tables and then read on.

Cost estimate: option 1	
Wind turbine: Marlec 910	320
Tower	100
PV panels (55W) or extra turbine	350
Controllers	200
Inverter (140W)	100
Batteries (4kWh)	450
Sundries (cables, etc.)	230
Total	**1,750**

Cost estimate: option 2	
Wind turbine: Proven 2.2kW	2,600
Tower	1,300
Controller	750
Inverter	1,700
Batteries (20kWh)	2,000
Sundries (cables, etc.)	1,500
Total	**9,850**

Option one: cutting back

This option relies on careful use of lighting, mainly using it in the evening, and assuming one main light in the living room (16W – approximately equivalent to a 75W bulb) and two smaller lights, say a reading lamp and one other are on most of the evening. It allows for a small monochrome TV, and a car-type stereo radio/cassette player. Both of these work directly on

DC from the storage batteries, giving the most efficient use of power as it avoids having to run the inverter to produce mains voltage. Sarah's sewing machine, however, needs mains, so a small inverter would be needed to feed it. If the machine had been a different type, it would have been possible to fit a DC motor to it and avoid the inverter altogether. However, if an inverter of a few hundred watts rating is chosen, it will be useful for powering other small appliances occasionally.

The big things that Sarah and Tom would have to do without are an electric cooker, an electric fridge, a washing machine, a vacuum cleaner, a hair-dryer, and Tom's computer. The cottage could be heated by a wood- or coal-fired stove/boiler that would also provide hot water and do most of the cooking. The fridge and cooker problem could be solved by buying bottled gas-powered ones.

The washing machine, hair-dryer, and vacuum cleaner are more difficult, as providing for them would push the system cost up significantly. The local launderette or a small standby generator for occasional heavy loads are possible solutions. Tom could swap his power-hungry computer for a lap-top that, with a DC power adaptor, would only consume a few watts and would probably not push the system size up significantly.

A small 72W wind turbine would probably do the job in winter; the Marlec 910 will give an average power of about 20W, given a mean wind speed of 5m/s. The well-exposed site above the cottage would probably maintain this mean speed in the winter months, but it would need checking before decisions were made.

In the summer, when wind speed is lower, the 910's output is probably too low even for the reduced summer load. For example, at 3m/s mean, it will only be giving an average output of 6W, well below the needed 11.4W average. The shortfall could be made up by adding a PV panel; a single 55W module would probably do the job. Alternatively, for a similar cost, a second Marlec 910 could be added, keeping it a purely wind system; this would double the winter energy available too, which of course the PVs would not. However, the supply reliability would definitely be better with the hybrid wind/PV system.

The overall cost of Option 1 would be around £2000, assuming that the Breezes did all the installation work themselves (see page155). This cost is lower than it would be at many other sites, because of the relatively high wind speed estimate.

Option two: business more as usual

This option allows for more lighting and more appliances. The load table is shown on the following page. The biggest impact on the energy demand comes from the addition of a fridge, which alone uses about three times the total energy needs of Option 1.

Some calculations were made and it was concluded that a wind turbine of 1–2kW would probably handle this option. Again, adding PVs (several hundred watts to be significant in this case) will give better summer supply reliability. A rough estimate of the costs of such a system was made (see page 155). The couple gulped, bid farewell to CAT, and went home to think about it.

Option 2 was clearly too expensive, so they decided to go for a small system initially, but with a view to expanding it when they could afford it. Armed with books from CAT's bookshop, they got into designing the electrics and producing a detailed plan...

Designing a system for option one

Sizing the system The energy requirements from the wind turbine/PV combination are 274Wh/day in summer and 377Wh/day in winter. The first step was to check how this compared to the energy available from wind and solar inputs on the site.

First they found some wind speed data for west coast UK; these are shown in the table opposite. This confirmed that a reasonable expectation was a mean wind speed of 5m/s over the year. There was, however, an uncertainty of about 20% on this figure between individual years – a point to be borne in mind when thinking about supply reliability. Also, the figures given in wind data publications are nearly always based on a measuring height of 10m, so the speeds must be corrected for the actual wind turbine tower height used. For a small Marlec machine a reasonable height would be 5m. In this case the correction factor will be 0.88.

Using wind speed data on page 162 and the performance data on page 160, the average energy produced per day was found for each month.

For example: January: Mean speed = 5.2 m/s

From table: 22W (interpolating between figures for 5 and 6 m/s)

Energy per day: 22W x 24 hrs = 528 Wh/d

Comparing these with the energy requirements shows that they are quite a good match. The winter need of 377Wh/day is met in a typical year

The Breezes' energy requirements option 2 – business more as usual

		LOAD		TIME Summer		TIME Winter	
Appliance	AC/DC	Number in use	Power watts	hrs/day	watt-hrs/day energy consumed	hrs/day	watt-hrs/day energy consumed
1 Low-energy lights	DC	3	16			x 12	= 576
2 Low-energy lights	DC	3	8			x 12	= 288
3 Low-energy lights	DC	2	16	x 5	= 160		
4 Low-energy lights	DC	2	8	x 5	= 80		
5 Radio	DC	1	2	x 8	= 16	x 8	= 16
6 **DC load consumption** (rows 1-5)					**256**		**880**
7 Colour TV	AC	1	50	x 3	= 150	x 6	= 300
8 Hi-fi	AC	1	25 (av.)	x 2	= 50	x 2	= 50
9 Sewing machine	AC	1	50	x 0.5	= 25	x 1	= 50
10 Hair-dryer (10mins / day / av.)	AC	1	800	x 0.17	= 136	x 0.17	= 136
11 Iron (10mins / day / av.)	AC	1	1000	x 0.17	= 170	x 0.17	= 170
12 Vac. cleaner (low power 10mins / day / av.)	AC	1	600	x 0.17	= 102	x 0.17	= 102

	LOAD			TIME Summer		TIME Winter	
Appliance	AC/DC	Number in use	Power watts	hrs/day	watt-hrs/day energy consumed	hrs/day	watt-hrs/day energy consumed
13 Fridge (fairly efficient)	AC	1	40 (av.)	x 24	= 960	x 24	= 960
14 Washing machine	AC	1	400	x 1	= 400	x 1	= 400
15 Computer (desktop)	AC	1	80	x 1	= 80	x 1	= 80
16 **AC load consumption** (rows 7-15)					**2073**		**2248**
17 Inverter losses (add 10% of AC load) *					207		225
18 Add standby loss for inverter (10W x 24 hours) *					240		240
19 Inverter input energy required (add rows 16, 17, 18)					2520		2713
20 Ad DC total from row 6 to give total DC consumption:					2776		3593
21 Add allowance for battery losses (approx. 25% of land)					694		898
22 **Total input of energy to battery needed (watt-hours per day)** (rows 20 +21)					**3470**		**4491**
23 Average power input needed (watt-hours / day / 24) (rows 22/24)					145W		187W

* Inverter losses are taken into account by adding 10% of the AC load (for a very efficient inverter such as the TRACE). It is necessary to add the standby loss of the inverter if it is left running all the time, as it is in this case.

from October to April, and the summer need of 274Wh/day is met in all but June, July and August. However, all these figures are rather marginal – a bigger safety margin should be aimed for. This is for three reasons. Firstly, long term variations in the wind speed – remember that the annual mean is likely to vary by, say, 20%. A 20% drop in mid-summer would reduce the already low figure of 230Wh/day by nearly one half. Secondly, it would cost a lot to provide more than a few days' battery storage, so there will be periods within each month, longer than the battery storage period, where the mean wind speed will be less than the monthly mean. Thirdly, they may have over-estimated the wind speed anyway.

However, as a point of principle, if you are trying to keep costs down and can be flexible over power use, it may be worth getting experience with a basic system such as this – it may be that you have underestimated the wind speed. One Marlec 910 could well be adequate.

The Breezes decided they were going to need some extra electrical input and checked up on what they could get from some PVs. Solar data for horizontal surfaces was found in the form of kWh/m^2 in daily averages for each month (see page 162). The figures given, strictly speaking, apply only to horizontally mounted panels, and the couple's south-facing roof is at 30° to the horizontal. However, in the UK's latitude this makes little difference to the actual radiation falling on the PV array. A south-facing tilt of up to 40° to the horizontal will give some benefit in collected energy over most of the year. There is hardly any improvement in mid-summer, maybe a 10% increase in

Average power output versus average wind speed, for a Marlec WG 910 (later 72W version) and typical UK wind speed distribution.	
Average wind speed (m/sec)	Average power (watts)
1	0.0
2	1.7
3	6.0
4	12.3
5	20.6
6	30.5
7	41.5
8	53.0

spring and autumn, potentially doubling or more in mid-winter, because the low-angle winter sun strikes the array at a much better angle compared to a horizontal array. However, much of this mid-winter benefit is usually lost because of shading due to trees, hills and other buildings. In summary, it is quite acceptable to use the horizontal surface figures directly even for a south-facing tilted surface. If there is serious shading, the figures must be adjusted accordingly.

These figures are numerically the same figures as for 'peak sunshine hours' (see the system design section), so an estimate of the energy output per day can be formed by simply multiplying the kWh/m^2 day figure by the peak power rating of the PV array. To account for energy losses (mainly due to mismatch between the battery voltage and the optimum PV array voltage), a typical efficiency factor of 0.85 is used. The figures looked encouraging – the PVs alone could almost supply the summer needs from May to July.

The next step was to add the solar and wind inputs together and then compare the totals with the energy needed (see table on page 162). These figures for total energy input looked much better, giving some safety margin over the required energy (274Wh/d summer and 377Wh/d winter). The worst months for safety margin in the combined wind/PV system are probably November and December. This suggested that the alternative solution of using two Marlec 910s or one larger wind turbine, rather than one PV panel, should be looked at. This would clearly give a big safety margin all year round, on the basis of the monthly figures calculated. However, long calm periods in the summer combined with the variation in monthly wind speeds from year to year suggests that this approach would probably give poorer supply reliability. Careful computer modelling would be necessary in order to compare the options properly. Sarah and Tom could not easily do this, so they simply decided to go for the wind/PV system, rather than put all their eggs into one basket by using two wind turbines.

Tom and Sarah picked a 55Wp PV module as a starting point.

Electrical storage

The Breezes were advised by CAT to design for about five days' storage. This meant that if the batteries were fully charged, they should be able to meet the winter load (377Wh/day) for five days with no input from wind or PVs and still only be 50% discharged. Therefore the total battery capacity

Wind speed data for west coast UK

	JAN	FEB	MAR	APR	MAY	JUN
Wind speed (m/s) at 10m above ground level	5.9	5.6	5.2	5	4.4	4.3
Wind speed (m/s) corrected for a tower at 5m	5.2	4.9	4.6	4.5	3.9	3.8
Average watt-hours per day produced by a Marlec 910	528	470	400	380	276	260

The solar contribution to the available energy

	JAN	FEB	MAR	APR	MAY	JUN
Solar radiation (kWh/m^{2}day) (Horiz)	0.47	0.95	2.2	3.2	4.4	4.7
Ideal daily output of 55W PV module (Wh/day)	26	52	121	176	242	258
Daily energy to battery (Wh/day) by a Marlec 910	22	44	103	150	206	219

Daily energy to battery for January: 0.47 x 55Wp x 0.85 = 22Wh/day

The total: available solar and wind power by month (watt-hours)

	JAN	FEB	MAR	APR	MAY	JUN
Solar: PV (Wh/d)	22	44	103	150	206	219
Wind: Marlec 910 (Wh/d)	528	470	400	380	276	260
Total (Wh/d):	**550**	**514**	**503**	**530**	**482**	**479**

JUL	AUG	SEP	OCT	NOV	DEC	Av.
4.3	4.1	4.4	5.3	5.3	5.5	5m/s
3.8	3.6	3.9	4.6	4.7	4.9	4.4m/s
260	230	276	400	420	470	

JUL	AUG	SEP	OCT	NOV	DEC
4.2	3.5	2.6	1.5	0.66	0.43
231	192	143	82	36	24
196	163	122	70	31	20

JUL	AUG	SEP	OCT	NOV	DEC
196	163	122	70	31	20
260	230	276	400	420	470
456	**393**	**398**	**470**	**451**	**490**

should be, at 12V, (377 x 5 x 2) /12V = 314Ah; in other words, three 100Ah 12V batteries at £150 each.

Electrical design

The first choice to be made was what voltage to use. With such a small system, it wasn't worth considering anything higher than 24V, so the choice was between 12V and 24V. 24V would reduce the cost of the cable from the wind turbine, give a slightly higher inverter efficiency, and would be beneficial if they expanded the system in the future, but would probably increase the battery cost and PV cost (because they would have to buy two smaller 12V modules). A 12V system would have the advantage of the easier availability of 12V appliances such as TVs, car radios, etc. They eventually decided to go for 12V and accept that there might be some additional cost in the future if they had to upgrade to 24V.

With the help of some books bought at CAT, Tom and Sarah worked out their electrical system. It looked like the block diagram on page 166. The following paragraphs use numbers referring to the diagram.

1. They would bring the power down the turbine tower with a 2.5m twin and earth cable. This is short so the voltage drop would not be a problem.

2. They would use a buried, waterproof steel-wire-armoured cable from a junction box at the base of the tower to the cottage. Consulting the voltage drop tables, they found that for their maximum power of 70W (approximately 5A at 14V), they needed a cable of about 10mm^2 to keep the voltage drop down to 2V. 100m of 10mm^2 armoured 2 core would cost them £205. However, they noticed that 4 core 4mm^2 cable was only £155/100m. If they connected this in two pairs, they would have 8mm^2 cable; the voltage drop would still not be too bad – say 2.5V – and they would save about £50. (It's worth shopping around for cable as prices can vary dramatically.) Having chosen their cable, the Breezes made sure that all outdoor connectors they were going to use would be waterproof and not prone to corrosion.

3. The cable from the PV module was much shorter – 8m – and the maximum current was estimated to be:

    $$\frac{55Wp}{12V} = 4.6A$$

    (In practice it will always be less than 4.6A as peak power is only achieved at higher module voltages – say, 14V.) For a 5% volt drop this would require 2.5mm^2 cable and for PVs this is the maximum advisable volt drop. As it was only an indoor short cable, cost was not so critical, so they decided to use 4mm^2 twin-and-earth for good measure.

4/5. The wind generator tower was quite exposed from the point of view of lightning strikes. It is important to minimise the likelihood of lightning surges entering the house, so several precautions should be taken:

i) Earth the base of the tower to a 1m copper-coated earth spike, driven into the ground just beside it.

ii) Earth the ends of all the metal guy wires thoroughly.

iii) Connect the cable armouring to the earth spike at the tower base.

iv) Drive another earth spike where the cable enters the cottage and connect the negative side of the power cable and the armouring to it.

v) Check that the regulators have built-in lightning protection.

This won't stop a direct hit, but will protect the circuit from high voltage induced transient spikes from nearby strikes.

6. A shunt regulator seemed the best way to control the wind generator output to avoid overcharging the battery. Tom and Sarah found that such a regulator was available specifically for the Marlec 910, and was quite cheap. The only problem would be that if the regulator were connected directly to the batteries and the battery voltage were forced up by the PVs or by an auxiliary battery charger, the regulator would attempt to dissipate all the input power – not just from the wind generator. As this regulator does not current limit, it is likely to burn out under these conditions. They were advised that the solution would be to fit a diode between the regulator and the battery to block current flow from the battery towards the regulator. A Schottky type 80SQ045 is a wire-ended 8A 45V diode that would be suitable and cheap at £1.50. The diode can be mounted in a terminal block, placed so that air can circulate freely around it, as the diode will get hot in periods of high wind. The regulator would now be measuring the battery voltage plus the diode drop (around 0.5V), so when ordering the regulator it became necessary to ask for its voltage to be set 0.5V higher than normal.

7. The PVs could also cause overcharging, particularly if the cottage was left empty during a summer holiday. A simple and fairly cheap

The Breezes' System

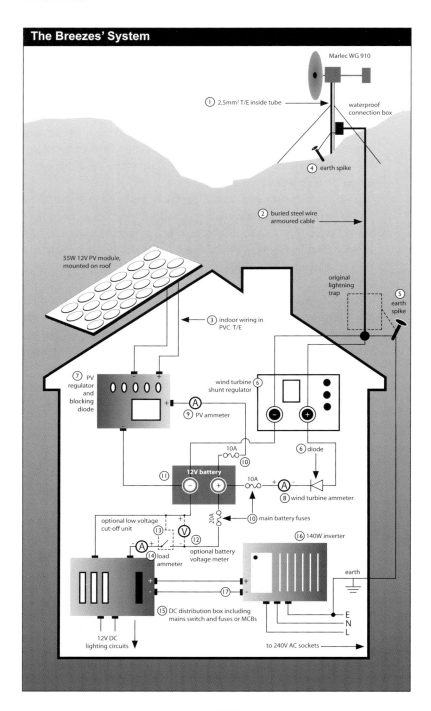

Marlec WG 910

① 2.5mm² T/E inside tube

waterproof connection box

④ earth spike

② buried steel wire armoured cable

55W 12V PV module, mounted on roof

original lightning trap

⑤ earth spike

③ indoor wiring in PVC T/E

⑦ PV regulator and blocking diode

wind turbine shunt regulator ⑥

⑨ PV ammeter

10A ⑩

⑥ diode

⑪ 12V battery

10A ⑧ wind turbine ammeter

optional low voltage cut-off unit

20A ⑩ main battery fuses

⑬ ⑫ optional battery voltage meter

⑯ 140W inverter

⑭ load ammeter

earth

⑮ DC distribution box including mains switch and fuses or MCBs

⑰

E
N
L

12V DC lighting circuits

to 240V AC sockets

relay controller was chosen to prevent this. It simply disconnects the PVs if the battery voltage goes too high. This controller included a blocking diode to avoid power flowing back from the batteries to the PVs at night. Alternatively, another 80SQ045 diode could be used for this vital function.

8/9. In order to check that the wind generator and PVs were working properly and to get some idea of the contribution each was making, the Breezes decided to fit two separate ammeters (8 and 9), each capable of reading up to 5A.

10. All wires from the positive battery terminal had to be protected from excess current, so three fuses were fitted about a meter away from the batteries. A car accessories fuse holder and fuses were used for this. (These are often of low quality and can cause problems. A small mains-type fuse-box with ceramic fuses would have been a better choice.)

11. Three 100Ah 12V batteries were needed and they were placed in what used to be an outside toilet. Tom and Sarah decided that this would give some protection from very low temperatures in winter, would keep any hydrogen gas out of the house, and would be easy to get at for maintenance. The wires to the meters and the DC distributor box were brought through a hole in the wall to a panel mounted close by, inside the house. The hole should be at a low level and sealed to prevent the ingress of gas into the house. The special large connectors for the battery terminals were obtained from the local garage.

12. The Breezes were also advised that a battery volt meter would be useful for getting a quick idea of the state-of-charge of the battery, so a volt meter with a 15V full scale reading was purchased. (A moving coil type is best for this.) All their meters were bought from Maplin (www.maplin.co.uk).

13. They decided to fit a low voltage cut-off. They felt they would prefer to keep a regular eye on the indoor volt meter and reduce consumption voluntarily if necessary, but the risk of damaging the expensive batteries made them decide to fit a low-voltage cut-off unit as a safety precaution (they bought one from Dulas Ltd. for £60).

14. They decided it was also worth fitting a load ammeter. To choose the rating of this, they had to add up the power ratings of all loads

that may be on at the same time and then divide the total wattage by 12V to get the maximum load current. They chose a 15A meter.

15. A normal mains consumer unit was used as the distribution and fuse box for the house wiring. This also provided a useful master switch. The lighting wiring used 4mm^2 cables to two central junction boxes, one in the roof space and one above the downstairs ceiling. The remaining wiring was 1.5mm^2. Sockets for 12V table lamps, TV, etc., used non-standard types (i.e. not the usual 13A flat pin type) to avoid confusion between mains and 12V appliances. Three-pin Euro connectors were chosen so that the TV and radio would not accidentally be plugged in with reversed polarity (they may be seriously damaged if positive and negative connections are reversed). The feeds to these sockets were fused at 6A so that fairly thin, 6A rated flexible cables to appliances would be safely protected.

16. Tom and Sarah didn't want to spend too much on an inverter, as it wouldn't be used very much, and if they upgraded the system later they would probably need a different type altogether. After some catalogue browsing, they picked a POW200 Powerstar inverter. It has an output rating of 140W continuous (with short peaks of two or three times this). Efficiency is claimed to be 90% at 100W, and it uses only 3W of standby power. The price quoted was around £100. They opted to fit a conveniently placed switch (capable of 20A) in its DC feed so that it could easily be turned off when not required. The inverter was sited indoors so it was less likely to suffer damp damage.

17. All the wiring from the batteries to the distribution board and the inverter should be chosen for very low volt drop, say 1% or 2% of battery voltage at the maximum current. Tom and Sarah reckoned that the total distance from the batteries to the inverter would be about 3 metres, so 16mm^2 cable was used. By carrying out the installation themselves, Tom and Sarah successfully completed the system for under £2000.

Case study 3
Nyahode School, Zimbabwe – a Diesel-Solar Hybrid System

Nyahode Union Learning Centre is a small secondary school in the Eastern Highlands of Zimbabwe. Located on the slopes of a small valley the grounds of the school have been planned using permaculture water-harvesting techniques implemented by the students. Since the nearest powerlines are several kilometres an independent power system was more cost effective than a grid connection. The headmaster raised money to install small solar lighting systems in teachers' houses to improve their standard of living.

The school has expanded its facilities to offer vocational training courses to school leavers in woodwork, metalwork, building skills, motor mechanics and textile and garment design. Since many of these subjects require the use of electrical tools and machinery, the school found funding for a large generator to provide three-phase power to the workshops. There was also a pressing need for lighting in classrooms to allow students to study at night, and sockets to power administrative computers, overhead projectors and a large TV and video for education and entertainment. Since the workshop equipment is only used for a few hours during the day, the school was faced with the prospect of running a 50kW generator in the evenings to provide about 1 kW of lighting and TV loads. Even with such a small load, the generator would use nearly two-thirds of the fuel it would burn at full load, creating very high running costs.

An early solution was to use separate solar PV lighting systems, but due to the dispersed location of buildings this would have required more than a dozen autonomous systems. A renewable energy engineer working for the Permaculture Training Centre based in Harare suggested an alternative plan combining solar and diesel power with an inverter/charger and a large battery bank. Excess power during generator hours is stored in the 24 volt (DC) battery bank and converted back into single phase 230 volt AC power by the inverter to supply low power, high value loads like lights, TV, video, refrigeration and computers at any time the generator is off.

During periods like weekends and holidays with no heavy loads requiring the generator, the battery bank is kept topped up by six solar photovoltaic (pv) modules governed by a charge controller.

Main Components

Inverter / Charger

The heart of the system is a Trace DC-AC inverter/AC-DC battery charger. This produces a sustained 230 volt 'modified sine-wave' AC output of 2.4kW but can handle short peak loads upto 8kW with auto-resetting overload protection. When no loads are present, it shuts down to a 'standby' consumption of less than 1 watt. Temperature and current compensated battery monitoring closes down the inverter when the battery bank reaches its lowest safe voltage, extending battery life considerably.

Immediately sensing the start-up of the generator, the inverter reverses function to become a 70 amp, 24 volt battery charger using a sophisticated three stage charging cycle ideally suited to deep-cycle batteries.

The inverter is sized to meet immediate expected loads, but can be supplemented by a second unit operating in tandem if future energy requirements expand further.

The main control board for Nyahode's power system, showing the inverter-charger, meters, transfer switch and distribution box.

Battery bank

The 'fuel-tank' or energy reservoir of the system is provided by two SEC vented deep-cycle batteries connected in series to give a capacity of 1400 amphours at 24 volts. These should last at least ten years with minimal maintenance at expected load levels. The bank stores enough power to supply full evening loads for over 4 days without input from either generator or solar in times of breakdown or poor weather. There is ample capacity to cater for future load increases and to absorb power from micro-hydro electric and wind turbines, both of which are included in the Centre's future plans.

Two vented deep-cycle batteries store 1400 amp-hours at 24V. A hinged cover protects the batteries, and the cables pass through the wall to the inverter and control equipment mounted next door.

Six PV modules are pole mounted outside the generator room.

Solar PV modules
Six Solarex 60Wp polycrystalline PV modules provide trickle charging for the battery bank during daylight hours.

Charge controller
To protect the battery bank from harmful overcharging, a Trace 30A Controller monitors the battery voltage and disconnects the PV modules when the batteries are fully charged. The controller includes a blocking diode to prevent power feeding back to the panels overnight.

Wiring and lights
Since the system operates exclusively at 230V AC the battery system feeds directly through the wiring and distribution unit provided for the generator. The inverter output is single phase, so priority low power loads such as the lights and selected sockets are connected to the red phase, whilst the generator provides three-phase supply to machine tools. Classrooms and offices were fitted with high efficiency compact fluorescent light fittings to reduce the inverter load.

Monitoring
In order to measure to monitor the performance of the system, readings are taken from several meters whenever the system is used. These cover battery voltage, generator running hours, power into and out of inverter and fuel and oil inputs. For a complete record, it is planned to add a watt-hour meter to measure the PV input directly.

Outcome
The diesel solar hybrid system was installed in February, 1996 and has made a considerable impact on the scope of facilities available to staff and pupils. During term time, the generator runs for few hours most weekdays, storing enough surplus power to run evening activities. In the holidays and weekends, the solar input is enough to maintain batteries for the reduced evening loads. During sustained periods of bad weather, the generator is occasionally run to top up the batteries, but it is hoped that the addition of more solar modules and a 750W wind turbine in the future will make this unnecessary. Since the addition of the battery-inverter system, generator use has been cut by 80% resulting in large fuel savings and vastly extending the generator's life.

Nyahode School – Load and system assessment

Appliance	LOADS AC/DC	Number in use	Power watts	TIME Hours of use per day	ENERGY Total energy consumed Wh/day
Light	DC	1	12W	x 2	= 24Wh
Total DC load load					**24Wh**
Lights, compact	AC	16	18W	x 3	= 864Wh
Lights, compact	AC	3	18W	x 6	= 324Wh
Television	AC	1	120W	x 3	= 360Wh
Video	AC	1	40W	x 1	= 40Wh
Power tools	AC	1	750W	x 0.5	= 375Wh
Computer	AC	1	120W	x 5	= 600Wh
Printer	AC	1	50W	x 1	= 50Wh
			Peak load **1116W**		Total AC load 2613Wh
Allowance for inverter loss (approx. 20% of load)					523Wh
Total inverter load					3136Wh
Total DC consumption					**3160Wh**
Allowances for battery losses (approx. 25% of load)					790Wh
Total daily energy required					**3950Wh**

Battery sizing

Days of reseve	4 days
Max depth of discharge	50%
Capacity required	31596Wh
At system voltage	24V
Actual battery bank	24V	1500Ah	1317Ah
Average daily discharge	11%

Energy Sources	No	Voltage	Current	Time/day	Whr/day
Diesel genset – battery charger	1	24V	70A	1.5hr	2520Wh
Polycrystalline PV modules	6	12V	4A	5hr	1440Wh
Total daily energy supplied					**3960Wh**

Nyahode School diesel -solar hybrid power system

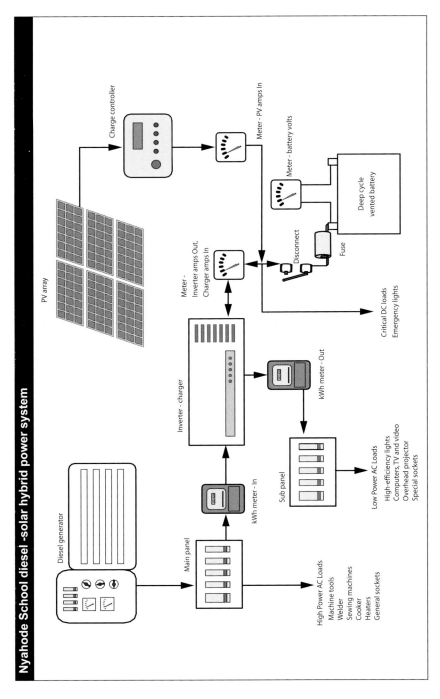

Case study 4
Mobile Home, UK

Several years ago, Dan and Mary left the insecurity of unscrupulous inner city landlords and welfare dependency to live off their wits on the road. By selling off the unnecessary trappings of former consumer lifestyles they raised enough money to buy an old but serviceable van. With a car stereo, paraffin lamps and candles they took to the hills and commons, enduring police harassment and small town prejudice to live a simpler life of summer festivals and long winter nights.

Dan bought a 12V soldering iron and started to make jewellery, while Mary found a hand sewing machine to make groovy hats and clothes. Needing extra light for winter working, they rigged up two 12V fluorescent lights from a caravan supplies shop to run off the van's battery. They soon found that their battery was running flat, and they were always in need of help to push-start the van.

Noticing the growing profusion of wind turbines and solar panels on vehicles at festivals they attended, they talked to 'people with screwdrivers' at a Techno Tribe installation. Following advice, they worked out their electrical loads and decided to invest their takings from the weekend's trading in a second-hand sealed battery, a voltmeter, some fuses and two amorphous PV panels from a renewable energy supplies stall. By the end of that summer they had saved enough for a small wind turbine with controller, which they added to the system. They found a split charging relay at a caravan supplier that enabled them to recharge the sealed battery from the vehicle alternator.

After the next winter the sealed battery gave up due to repeated flattening, so the following summer's takings were invested in a new battery and a low-voltage disconnect unit. With a growing interest in mobile systems and the need for renewable power, Dan copied a simple cycle generator he had seen powering a sound system. In preparation for the upcoming season they decided to sell the amorphous panels and invest in a 55Wp crystalline module.

Prior to purchasing the crystalline module, their system worked something like this:

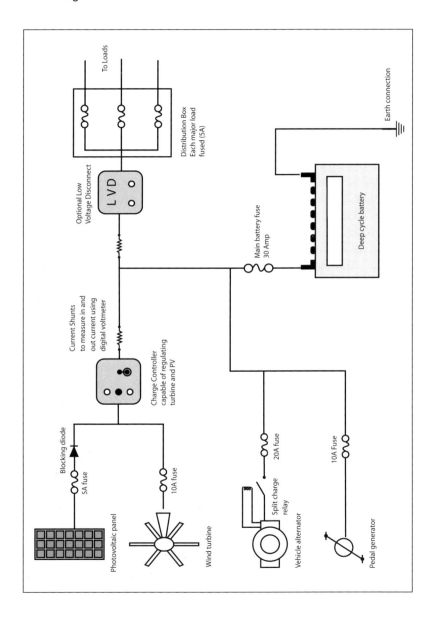

System sizing

As already stated, the unpredictability of a travelling lifestyle makes system sizing a very approximate exercise. At best, it can give an indication of how much power is required to meet an ideal load situation, and show the relative effect of different components. It can be seen from the costing and sizing that the wind turbine is the most expensive component, but provides most of the power input. It is also the most unpredictable, since wind resources are far more site specific than solar. Wind speeds tend to be significantly higher in winter, and Dan and Mary tend to stay put for longer periods, enabling them to arrange for a higher tower.

The key to mobile systems is versatility – adjusting loads to suit the resources available. In the summer, more time is spent outside or travelling, so demand is low and there is frequent input to the battery from the split charge system. In the winter, nights are long and time is spent working inside, greatly increasing the loads. In this circumstance, the pedal generator provides a valuable back-up, especially if they do not move for several weeks at a time. Of course, if the battery gets desperately low, it is always possible to run the van engine for half an hour – not very cost effective but a reassuring fall-back. The system as described would probably benefit from the addition of another battery, since the 2 day storage capacity for winter loads is very low.

Rough costing	
Marlec Rutland 910-913, new	470
Charge controller	150
Tower, guys, scrap	50
PV modules, 2nds	50
Battery, gel, new	100
Voltmeter, 2nd hand	10
Low voltage disconnect	50
Pedal generator, scrap	50
Split charge relay	20
Wiring, fuses, etc, 2nd hand	20
12V lights	50
Total	**820**

Mobile Domestic System sizing table

	LOAD		TIME Summer		TIME Winter	
Appliance	Number in use	Power watts	hrs/day	Wh/day energy consumed	hrs/day	Wh/day energy consumed
Halogen spots	2	10	x 1hr	= 20Wh	x 2hr	= 40Wh
Fluorescent lights	2	8	x 0.3hr	= 5Wh	x 2hr	= 32Wh
LED strings	2	0.1	x 2hr	= 0.4Wh	x 6hr	= 1Wh
Stereo	1	10	x 8hr	= 80Wh	x 10hr	= 100Wh
Television	1	35	x 1hr	= 35Wh	x 2hr	= 70Wh
Sewing machine	1	20	x 1hr	= 20Wh	x 3hr	= 60Wh
Soldering iron	1	30	x 0.2hr	= 5Wh	x 1hr	= 30Wh
				165Wh		**333Wh**
Generators						
PV	2	8	x 4hr	= 64Wh	x 1hr	= 8Wh
Wind turbine	1	70	x 2hr	= 140Wh	x 4hr	= 280Wh
Pedal generator	1	80	x 0hr	= 0Wh	x 0.5hr	= 40Wh
Charger	1	200	x 0.5hr	= 100Wh	x 0.3hr	= 60Wh
				304Wh		**388Wh**
Net charge				**139Wh**		**55Wh**

Batteries	No.	Volts	Amphours	Watt Hours		
Sealed gel	1	12V	100Ah	1200Wh		
Max depth of discharge		60%	60Ah	720Wh		
Days storage				Summer 4 days		Winter 2 days

Glossary

alternating current (AC): electric current in which the direction of flow changes at frequent, regular intervals. Eg mains.

alternator: a generator that produces alternating current such as those found in most vehicles.

amorphous silicon: a type of thin film PV silicon cell having no crystalline structure.

ambient temperature: the average temperature of the surrounding area.

ampere (amp A): unit of electric current which measures the flow of electrons per unit of time.

ampere hour (amp-hour Ah): a measure of total charge commonly used to indicate energy capacity of batteries. One amp-hour is equal to the quantity of charge in the flow of one ampere over one hour.

anemometer: a device like a weathervane, with cups that cause it to spin round in the wind, used to measure the wind's velocity.

antimony: an electricity-conducting metal used in some batteries.

appliance: a device, such as radio or television, which consumes electricity.

armoured cable: multiple core electrical cable commonly used for buried and external applications. The insulated conductors are surrounded by sheath of metal wires to protect them from accidental damage.

array: an assembly of several PV modules on a support structure together with associated wiring.

ballast inverter: a device which converts low voltage direct current to the type of high voltage AC current required by fluorescent lamps.

battery: a device that stores and releases electrical energy by means of the electrochemical reaction of its active materials.

battery capacity: the total number of amp-hours that can be removed from a fully-charged battery or cell at a specified discharge rate.

biomass: organic material of any type, such as wood, plants, straw, or refuse.

blocking diode: a solid-state electrical device placed in circuit between the module and the battery to prevent discharge of the battery when the voltage of the battery is higher than that of the module (i.e. at night).

by-pass diode: a solid-state electrical device installed in parallel with modules of an array which allows current to by-pass a shaded or damaged module.

cell (battery): the smallest unit or section of a battery that can store electrical energy and that is capable of providing a current to an external load.

cell (photovoltaic): see solar cell.

charge controller: a device which protects the battery, load and array from voltage fluctuations, alerts the users to system problems and performs other management functions.

charge current: electric current supplied to and stored in a battery.

circuit: a system of conductors (i.e. wires and appliances) capable of providing a closed path for electric current.

circuit diagram: a special type of drawing used by electricians to represent electric circuits.

connector strips: insulated screw-down wire clamps used to fasten wires together.

converter: a device that converts a DC voltage source to a higher or lower DC voltage.

crystalline silicon cell: a type of PV cell made from a single crystal or polycrystalline slice of silicon.

current (amps, amperes) (A): the rate of flow of electrons through a circuit.

cycle: one discharge and charge period of a battery.

cycle life: of a battery, the number of cycles it is expected to perform before being reduced to 80% of its rated capacity.

days of storage: the number of consecutive days a stand-alone system will meet a defined load without energy input.

deep discharge (or cycle) battery: a type of battery that is not damaged when a large portion of its energy capacity is repeatedly removed.

depth of discharge: a measure in percentage of the amount of energy removed from the battery during a cycle.

diffuse radiation: solar radiation that reaches the earth indirectly due to reflection and scattering.

diode: an electrical semiconductor 'one-way valve', rated for maximum voltage and current. A voltage drop of 0.3 to 2V is created across the diode when current flows through it.

diode string: diodes connected in series to reduce voltage by a defined amount.

direct current (DC): electric current flowing in one direction.

direct radiation: radiation coming in a beam from the sun. It can be focussed, and casts sharp shadows.

discharge: the removal of electric energy from a battery.

dump load: an electrical load, usually some form of air or water heater, that is used by a battery charge controller or hydro load controller to dissipate excess power.

dynamo: a generator that produces DC current through use of a commutator, commonly found on old vehicles.

E=mc²: Einstein's famous equation that says that the energy (E) in a given amount of matter is equivalent to its mass (m) multiplied by the speed of light (c = 186,000 miles per second) squared.

efficiency: the ratio of output power (or energy) to input power (or energy) expressed as a percentage.

electric power: the rate at which energy is supplied from an electricity generating source or consumed by a load. It is measured in watts (W).

electrolyte: a conducting liquid in a battery, in which the flow of electric current takes place by the migration of ions from plate to plate. Lead-acid batteries use a sulphuric acid electrolyte.

equalising charge: a charge well above the normal 'full' charge of a battery which causes the electrolyte inside the cells to bubble and get mixed up, and fully charges cells which tend otherwise to charge imperfectly.

field coils: coils of wire in a motor or generator that create a magnetic field when current flows through them (see also 'permanent magnets').

field effect transistor (FET): a semiconductor 'switch', which operates either fully on or off (i.e. non-linearly) and is used in many modern amplifiers and controllers.

float voltage: a battery should be kept at the float voltage to complete and maintain a full charge without excessive gassing.

fluorescent tube: a highly efficient light using a high voltage discharge through a glass tube filled with gas. Requires fittings that include circuitry that starts and maintains the discharge. Produces about five times as much light as an equivalently powered tungsten filament bulb and last five times longer.

frequency: cycles per second (measured in hertz).

fuse: a device which protects circuits and appliances in the system from damage by short circuits or overloading.

gassing: the emission of hydrogen gas from a battery caused by the chemical reactions inside it. The hydrogen is flammable, and so dangerous, and needs to be safely dispersed. May be violent and cause battery damage if voltage is too high during charging.

gel battery: a type of sealed deep-cycle lead-acid battery where the electrolyte (acid) is in the form of a jelly surrounding the lead plates. Particularly suitable for mobile applications since there is no danger of acid spills.

halogen bulb: an efficient light consisting of a conducting filament in a bulb filled with a halogen gas. Produces about twice as much light as an equivalent tungsten bulb.

head: in a water power (hydro) system, the vertical distance in metres from the intake pipe to the turbine wheel. Generally, the more head there is the more power is available.

heat shrink : a versatile insulating material in the form of a plastic tube that is placed over exposed conductors and shrinks to fit when heated.

hybrid system: an electricity generating system that uses more than one type of generator as its source; commonly a wind turbine and PV array, or any renewable source and a diesel generator as a back-up.

hydrometer: a tool that indicates the state of charge of lead-acid batteries by measuring the thickness of the acid inside its cells.

I-V curve: the plot of current versus voltage characteristics of a solar cell, module or array. I-V curves are used to compare various solar cell modules, and to determine their performance at various levels of insolation and temperature.

insolation: incident solar radiation. A measure of the solar energy incident on a given area over a specified period of time. Usually expressed in kilowatt-hours per square metre per day or indicated in peak sun hours.

inverter: a device which changes a DC input current into an AC output current using an electrical transformer and electronic switches.

kilowatt (kW): one thousand watts. Standard unit for measuring electrical power.

kilowatt-hour (kWh): energy equivalent to one thousand watts delivered for the period of one hour. Standard unit for measuring electrical energy.

lead-acid battery: a battery, like a car battery, containing lead plates and sulphuric acid as the electrolyte.

leisure batteries: a type of lead-acid battery better suited to deep discharge.

light-emitting diode (LED): a type of diode that lights up when current is flowing through it. Commonly used as an indicator in numerous electrical appliances and and as a source of low-level decorative lighting.

linear control device: can vary smoothly between on and off.

load: the set of equipment or appliances (lights, 'fridge, tv, radio) that uses the electrical power from the generating source, battery or module.

loss of power probability (LOPP): a statistical indicator of a stand-alone system's likelihood of running out of power. Often used in design software for critical non-domestic applications such as medical refrigeration, signalling and telecommunications.

low voltage cut-out: a feature of some charge controllers that cuts off power to the load when the battery reaches a low state of charge.

MCBs: Miniature circuit breakers – used instead of fuses to protect cables or equipment from high current.

modified sine wave: a term used by several inverter manufacturers to describe an AC output wave created by combining two or more square waves. Generally cheaper and more efficient than many pure sine wave inverters, and more versatile than square wave ones.

nuclear fusion: the bringing together of (positively-charged) atomic nuclei to release a huge amount of nuclear energy; the opposite of nuclear fission.

ohm (Ω): a unit of electrical resistance.

Ohm's Law (V=IR): a fundamental electrical relationship equating voltage to the sum of current and resistance in an electrical element.

overcharging: leaving batteries on charge after they have reached their full (100%) state of charge. Potentially damaging to battery life.

parallel connection: joining two or more loads or sources, positive to positive, negative to negative, so that their individual currents are added but the overall voltage remains constant (see also 'series connection').

peak power (Wp): the amount of power a PV module can be expected to deliver under maximum sunshine conditions.

photovoltaic (PV) device: a device that converts light energy into electric energy.

permanent magnet: a material that requires no current to maintain its magnetism. When used in motors and generators, it tends to increase efficiency as no current is used to create the required magnetic field.

plate: in a battery, a sheet of metal such as lead or antimony.

Pmax: the maximum amount of power.

polarity connection: in DC systems incorporating batteries, equipment must be connected with the correct polarity so that positive (+ve) connects to positive and negative (-ve) to negative contacts.

potential difference (voltage V): the difference in potential around a circuit is the 'push' that causes current to flow. Measured in volts (V).

power conditioning (unit – PCU): electrical equipment used to convert DC power from a generator or battery into a form suitable for the loads.

RCCBs: residual current circuit breakers – protect against electric shock by monitoring current flow in live and neutral conductors. Any discrepancy represents a potentially hazardous earth leakage and causes the breaker to trip.

RCD : Residual current device – an alternative name for an RCCB (above).

recombination caps: small caps that fit on some vented batteries and recombine the hydrogen and oxygen gases given off during overcharging back to water, thereby reducing the frequency of electrolyte topping up.

rectifier: a semiconductor device, usually incorporating four diodes to convert AC to DC.

regulator: an electrical device that controls the voltage and/or current from a generator.

relay: an electrically operated mechanical switch, particularly suited to switching the large currents typical in many low-voltage systems.

resistance: the property of a conductor (i.e. a wire or appliance) that opposes the flow of current through it and converts electrical energy into heat. Resistance has the symbol R, and is measured in ohms, Ω.

rms: 'Root mean square' – used to give the effective voltage of a wave form; e.g. 240V mains is the rms voltage, not the peak voltage, which is 340V. It is equal to 71% of the instantaneous peak value (for a sine wave).

Schottky diode: a type of diode with low voltage drop, typically 0.3 to 0.5V. Ideal for use as a PV blocking diode.

sealed battery: these are deep-cycle batteries that have their electrolyte permanently sealed into the casing making transport safe and avoiding the need for topping up. Gel and nickel based batteries are examples.

series connection: joining two or more loads or sources, positive to negative, so that their individual voltages are added but the overall current remains constant (see also 'parallel connection').

self-discharge: charge lost from batteries left standing due to reactions within the cells and leakage current.

shallow discharge batteries: batteries designed to supply high power for a short duration; taking too much energy out of these batteries before recharging them is likely to damage the plates inside (eg, car batteries).

short circuit current: the current which flows when a generator's terminals are connected directly together so that its output voltage is zero.

silicon: a semi-conductor material commonly used to make photovoltaic cells and many electronic components.

sine wave: smooth cyclical variation in the effect of a phenomenon, plotted on a graph against time.

sinusoidal: in the manner of a sine wave.

solar cell: a device made from semiconductor material (e.g. silicon) which converts light energy into electric energy.

solar cell module: groups of encapsulated solar cells framed in glass or plastic units, usually the smallest unit of solar electric equipment available to the consumer.

solar incident angle: the angle at which the incoming solar beam strikes a surface.

solenoid: an electrical device for producing a push or pull mechanical force.

specific gravity: the ratio of the weight of a solution (i.e. battery acid) to an equal volume of water at a specified temperature. Used as an indicator of battery state-of-charge.

square wave: the simplest AC waveform, produced by cheaper inverters.

stand-alone electric system: an electric system which is not connected to the grid.

state of charge: the amount of charge in a battery expressed as a percentage of its rated charge capacity.

system voltage: the voltage at which the charge controller, lamps and appliances in a system operate, and at which the generator(s) and battery are configured.

telemetry: method of recording data and then signalling it to a distant point.

temperature compensation: a feature of more advanced charge controllers which makes allowance for the effect of temperature on the fully charged voltage of a battery.

terminal voltage: the voltage (or potential difference) between the positive and negative terminals of a battery or the terminals of a generator.

thyristor: solid state semiconductor switch available in very high current ratings.

total daily system energy requirement: the amount of energy required to meet the daily electrical load plus the extra energy required to overcome system energy losses.

Triac: semiconductor device similar to a thyristor but allows current to flow in both directions.

trickle charge: a low current charge. When the batteries are fully charged, some charge controllers reduce the energy from the generator to the battery to a trickle charge so that the batteries are not overcharged, but so that they still get enough current to overcome self-discharge.

tungsten filament bulb: cheap but inefficient light that produces illumination from a white hot conducting wire enclosed in an evacuated glass bulb or tube. Most energy is lost as heat.

twin and earth: electrical cable commonly used for internal domestic supply, consisting of two insulated copper conductors and a bare earth wire all encased in an outer sheath of PVC insulation.

VA rating: the rms voltage times rms current in an AC system. It is equal to power for heating loads and filament lamps but may be up to twice the power for motors.

volt (V): a unit of measurement of the force given to electrons in an electric circuit (see potential difference).

volt (or voltage) drop: loss of voltage and power due to resistance of the wire to the flow of electricity in long runs of cable.

watt (W): the internationally accepted measurement of power. One thousand watts are a kilowatt, and a million watts are a megawatt.

watt-hour (Wh): a common energy measure arrived at by multiplying the power times the amount of time used. Grid power is ordinarily sold and measured in kilowatt- (one thousand watts) hours.

waveform: a graph showing variation of amplitude of electrical signal against time.

Resources

Further reading
IEE On Site Guide: B57671: 2001 incorporating amendments
1 & 2, 2004
(The IEE wiring regulations), 16th edition IEE Publications,
£49.00, ISBN 978-0-86341-373-5
The Energy Saving House, 2nd edition, Salomon & Bedel,
CAT Publications, £12.00, ISBN 978-1-902175-55-3
Going With the Flow, Billy Langley and Dan Curtis,
CAT Publications, £12.00, ISBN 1-89804-918-1
Solar Water Heating: A DIY Guide, Paul Trimby,
CAT Publications, £7.99, ISBN 1-90217-530-1
Tapping the Sun, Chris Laughton,
CAT Publications, £7.99, ISBN 1-90217-529-8
Windpower Workshop, Hugh Piggott,
Cat Publications, £12.00, ISBN 1-89804-927-0
www.cat.org.uk/pubs – for pay per view directories of
companies supplying and installing renewable energy systems

Useful websites
www.standardsdirect.org (for parts of BS no. standards)

Seasonal power output:
PV Potential Estimation Utility
http://re.jrc.cec.eu.int/pvgis/apps/pvest.php
www.retscreen.net
www.metoffice.gov.uk tel: 08709000100/ 01392 885681

Alternative Energy for outdoor events:
Campaign for Real Events, www.c-realevents.demon.co.uk
www.fireflysolar.co.uk, renewable energy sources for outdoor
events.

Rinky Dink, bicycle powered sound system,
www.rinky-dink.org
tel: 01285 760413
Sunny Jim's Solar Powered Cabaret Stage,
www.myspace.com/sunnyjimstage
www.groovymovie.org
www.powabyke.com

General
Centre for Alternative Technology Information Office,
tel: 01654 705989 – for inquiries as to local suppliers of
renewable energy systems and/or equipment
Centre for Alternative Technology Consultancy Office,
tel: 01654 705974 – for feasibility studies or system design
advice, system design and installation

Index